W9-CTG-366

STUDENT STUDY GUIDE TO ACCOMPANY

BUSINESS
LAW

STUDENT STUDY GUIDE TO ACCOMPANY

BUSINESS LAW

FIFTH EDITION

JOHN W. WYATT, S.J.D.

Professor of Business Law
University of Florida
Member of Florida and Federal Bars

MADIE B. WYATT, A.B., LL.B.

Member of Florida and Federal Bars

McGraw-Hill Book Company

*New York St. Louis San Francisco Auckland Düsseldorf Johannesburg
Kuala Lumpur London Mexico Montreal New Delhi Panama Paris
São Paulo Singapore Sydney Tokyo Toronto*

This book was set in Caledonia by Monotype Composition Company, Inc.
The editors were Thomas H. Kothman and Joseph F. Murphy;
the cover was designed by J. E. O'Connor;
the production supervisor was Thomas J. LoPinto.
The Whitlock Press, Inc., was printer and binder.

Student Study Guide to accompany BUSINESS LAW

Copyright © 1975 by McGraw-Hill, Inc. All rights reserved.
Formerly published under the title of STUDENT WORKBOOK TO ACCOMPANY
BUSINESS LAW, copyright © 1971 by McGraw-Hill, Inc. All rights reserved.
Printed in the United States of America. No part of this publication may be reproduced,
stored in a retrieval system, or transmitted, in any form or by any means, electronic,
mechanical, photocopying, recording, or otherwise, without the prior written permission of
the publisher.

ISBN 0-07-072146-7

567890 WHWH 798

CONTENTS

PART NINE SECURITIES REGULATION; ANTITRUST; LABOR RELATIONS

PART TEN PROPERTY

PART ELEVEN WILLS AND TRUSTS

PART TWELVE INSURANCE; SURETYSHIP; GUARANTY; BANKRUPTCY

HOW TO USE THE STUDY GUIDE

The purpose of this study guide is to assist you with your study of business law. The answers to the questions and problems have been placed in the last part of the study guide so that you may know if you have arrived at the correct answers.

You will be learning principles of law, but the principles will be meaningless unless you develop the ability to apply the principles to given statements of facts. The problems in the study guide, in addition to the cases, end-of-chapter problems, and illustrations in the textbook, are designed to help you develop this ability. It should be kept in mind, however, that it is not the purpose of the textbook or the study guide to prepare you to be your own attorney, to be an expert in legal procedure, or to be able to draft your own legal documents. The purpose is to present legal rules in such a way that you will acquire a knowledge of law, apply this knowledge to your future profession, and seek the aid of an attorney when it becomes appropriate to do so.

Each chapter in the study guide contains a short introduction explaining the corresponding chapter in the textbook and, where appropriate, how the subject matter is related to earlier and later chapters. Forms of drafts and promissory notes have been reproduced in Chapter 20, "Form and Interpretation," to enable you to gain an insight into commercial paper as nearly as possible by practical application.

If you have already developed your own distinctive method of using a study guide, you should let your experience determine how you will use this study guide. If, however, you do not have a preferred method in mind, the following procedure is recommended to enable you to make the most effective use of your time and energy.

1. Read the introductions to the chapters in the study guide carefully. This reading will apprise you of what is contained in the chapter.

2. Examine the fill-in questions, and then proceed to read the textual material and cases in the textbook slowly. It is important that you read the particular case immediately after reading the section in the textbook illustrated by the case. The case frequently will illustrate the rules in the section.

3. Complete the fill-in questions without referring to the answers in the last part of the book. These questions are designed to assist you in learning important words and terms, the majority of which consists of new vocabulary. Moreover, you must have these questions properly completed because you will be using many of the words in later chapters.

4. Answer the problems in the study guide. These problems, coupled with the problems in the textbook, are specifically designed to give you experience in recognizing legal problems, analyzing factual situations, reaching a definite decision, and supporting your decision with the appropriate rules of law. Therefore, you should also prepare your answers to the problems in the textbook at this time.

5. Answer the true-false questions. These questions are an excellent method of learning principles of law. The false questions, however, should be restated in the form of true questions. This is particularly necessary if you intend to use the questions and problems in the study guide and the cases and end-of-chapter problems in the textbook for review.

6. Your teacher will give you the expected answers to the end-of-chapter problems in the textbook. If you have incorrect answers, you should immediately correct your answers. Your study of business law will become burdensome if you fail to have the correct answers chapter by chapter.

John W. Wyatt
Madie B. Wyatt

STUDENT STUDY GUIDE TO ACCOMPANY
BUSINESS LAW

INTRODUCTION ⌐

The purpose of Part 1 is to introduce you, the student, to the origin, growth, and source of law; to help you develop an understanding of the function of the courts in our legal system and the procedure followed in the trial and appeal of a case; and to acquaint you with the nature of torts and crimes. Part 1 lays the groundwork for the remaining chapters in the text, and contains numerous definitions. You should learn these definitions now. They will be used throughout the text, and you will need to understand them if you are to understand the chapters that follow.

CHAPTER 1
NATURE AND SOURCE
OF BUSINESS LAW

Fill-in Questions. Write the correct word or words in the blank spaces to complete the following statements.

1. The doctrine of _____ declares that once a decision is reached by a superior court in a particular case it becomes a precedent and all other cases of a similar kind are to be decided according to the same rule.
2. Technical forms of actions under the strict common-law practice were known as actions _____ and _____.
3. Justice, rather than custom, is the basis of _____.
4. An equitable doctrine which is intended to discourage stale demands is known as _____.
5. The remedy of _____ is frequently used in the winding up of a partnership.
6. A suit for _____ is available for the division of property held by two or more persons as co-owners.

7. A decree for _____ is a means of compelling a person to do precisely what he ought to have done under the terms of a contract.

8. A suit for _____ may be brought to remove a cloud on a title of real property.

9. Courts of equity will grant a decree for the _____ or _____ of a contract where the injured party entered into the contract because of duress.

10. The remedy of _____ is used to restrain persons from committing an act which appears to be against equity.

11. The origin of our partnership law was the _____.

12. The system of jurisprudence which was administered in the Roman Empire was the _____ law.

13. The branch of law which is concerned with the state is _____, and the law administered between private individuals is _____.

14. The law which regulates rights and duties is _____ law, and _____ law, or _____ law, provides a method for enforcing and maintaining rights and duties.

15. The _____ law emanates from the judicial branch of the government, and _____ law emanates from the legislative branch of the government.

16. The activities of the cities, towns, and villages are regulated by the enactment of _____.

17. The power of the _____ agencies may be administrative, legislative, judicial, or investigatory.

18. The Uniform Commercial _____ is intended to make uniform the law pertaining to commercial transactions among the various jurisdictions.

True-False Questions. *Indicate whether each of the following statements is true or false by circling the T or F.*

T　F　1. The technical common-law forms of action are used widely today.

T　F　2. "Equity aids the vigilant, not those who sleep on their rights" is the equitable maxim upon which the doctrine of laches was founded.

T　F　3. Substantive law regulates rights and duties.

T　F　4. The state constitutions compose the law of the land.

T　F　5. The term "common law" is used to distinguish the common law from equity.

T　F　6. Ordinances are enacted for the purpose of regulating the counties.

2

Name _____ **Date** _____

Problems. In the space provided, state your answer to the following.

1. Why was it necessary for the chancellor to organize a court of equity?

    _____

    _____

    _____

    _____

    _____

    _____

2. What was the origin of business law in the United States?

    _____

    _____

    _____

    _____

    _____

    _____

    _____

3. Explain how the administrative agencies are created.

    _____

    _____

    _____

    _____

    _____

    _____

4. Explain the distinction between public and private law.

    _____

    _____

    _____

    _____

    _____

    _____

5. Brown, who owed Jones and four other persons $1,000 each, assigned all of his assets to the payment of the four other persons. Jones knew of the transaction but failed to assert his right for over ten years. Explain the doctrine that will prevent Jones from setting aside the transaction.

_____

_____

_____

_____

_____

_____

_____

_____

_____

_____

_____

CHAPTER 2
THE JUDICIAL SYSTEM

Fill-in Questions. Write the correct word or words in the blank spaces to complete the following statements.

1. The United States _____ Court has the power to invalidate any federal or state statute by declaring it to be contrary to the United States Constitution.

2. A _____ corporation must appoint some local agent upon whom process may be served.

3. The United States courts of _____ do not have original jurisdiction.

4. The summons is served upon the defendant by _____ service or by _____ service.

5. The United States _____ courts are the trial courts in the federal judicial system.

6. The defendant is brought within the control of the court by the service of a _____ of process, frequently known as a _____.

7. The _____ court is the court of final resort in the state judicial system.

8. The power of a court to hear and determine a controversy is known as _____.

9. In many states, unnecessary litigation during the trial of a case may be eliminated by the judge and the attorneys during a _____ conference.

10. The person against whom a legal proceeding is brought is called the _____ or _____.

11. The person who institutes a legal proceeding is, in most states, called the _____ or _____.

12. The issuance of a writ of _____ is a method of seizing the property of a debtor and holding it in advance of a final judgment.

13. The doctrine of _____ prevents the rights, questions, and issues from being litigated more than once by the parties.

14. A writ of _____ is a means of seizing and selling the property of a debtor in order to satisfy a judgment.

15. The third person against whom garnishment proceedings are brought is called the _____.

True-False Questions. Indicate whether each of the following statements is true or false by circling the T or F.

T   *F*   1.   The procedure in the federal and state courts is quite similar.
T   *F*   2.   Special courts are found in all states to meet municipal and other particular problems.
T   *F*   3.   There is one court of final resort in most of the states.
T   *F*   4.   The decisions of the United States district courts are reported in the Federal Reporter.
T   *F*   5.   A person who institutes a legal proceeding is, in most states, called the respondent.
T   *F*   6.   The decision reached by the jurors in the trial of a case is known as the judgment.

Problems. In the space provided, state your answer to the following.

1.   Enumerate some of the courts in the state judicial system.

_____

_____

_____

_____

_____

_____

2.   Enumerate the courts in the federal system of courts.

_____

_____

_____

_____

_____

_____

3. Explain when a writ of execution may be issued.

_____

_____

_____

_____

_____

_____

_____

_____

_____

_____

_____

4. What is the function of the district court of appeals in the state system of courts?

_____

_____

_____

_____

_____

_____

_____

_____

_____

_____

_____

_____

5. Brown, who owed Jones $20,000, was attempting to assign all of his assets to Smith in order to avoid paying Jones. Explain the remedy that is available to Jones.

_____

_____

_____

_____

_____

_____

_____

_____

6. Explain the function of garnishment.

_____

_____

_____

_____

_____

_____

_____

7. Explain the procedure of the appellate courts.

_____

_____

_____

_____

_____

_____

_____

_____

CHAPTER 3
THE NATURE OF
TORTS AND CRIMES

Fill-in Questions. Write the correct word or words in the blank spaces to complete the following statements.

1. The law of torts pertains to _____ wrongs.
2. An _____ owes his _____ the duty of furnishing him with reasonably safe premises.
3. An unlawful refusal by a bailee to surrender the property to the rightful owner upon his demand amounts to _____.
4. A wrong which arises from an unwarranted use of property lawfully occupied by one person which restricts the ordinary use of property lawfully occupied by another person signifies a _____.
5. The actual unlawful use of force or violence signifies a _____.
6. _____ imprisonment may result from any acts which deprive a person of his personal liberty, provided the detention is unlawful.
7. _____ is understood to mean the offense of injuring the reputation of a person by _____ or _____.
8. The name of the action brought to recover damages for fraud is _____.
9. As a general rule, _____ is the proper remedy to recover the possession of every kind of chattel.
10. The law of _____ pertains to offenses against the state.

True-False Questions. Indicate whether each of the following statements is true or false by circling the T or F.

T   *F*   1. An owner of premises owes no duty to trespassers because of the "attractive nuisance" doctrine.

T   *F*   2. A person who enters upon the property of another for his own convenience with the consent of the owner is known as a licensee.

T   *F*   3. Driving cattle wrongfully over the land of another constitutes trespass.

T   *F*   4. Slander may be expressed by pictures.

T   *F*   5. A failure on the part of the injured party to use reasonable care will generally defeat an action for negligence on the ground of contributory negligence.

T   *F*   6.   A battery is the actual unlawful use of force or violence.
T   *F*   7.   The law of crimes pertains to civil wrongs.
T   *F*   8.   A nuisance signifies an unlawful act which deprives a person of possession of his personal property.
T   *F*   9.   Replevin is a possessory action.
T   *F*   10. The law of torts pertains to offenses against the state.

Problems. *In the space provided, state your answer to the following.*

1. What are the more significant forms of trespass?

_____

_____

_____

_____

_____

_____

_____

2. Enumerate some offenses which are commonly classified as felonies.

_____

_____

_____

_____

_____

_____

_____

3. Enumerate some of the offenses which are commonly classified as misdemeanors.

_____

_____

_____

_____

_____

_____

_____

_____

_____

_____

_____

4. What is the chief distinction between defamation and deceit?

_____

_____

_____

_____

_____

_____

_____

_____

_____

_____

_____

_____

_____

_____

5. What is the mutual benefit test used to distinguish an invitee from a licensee?

_____

_____

_____

_____

_____

_____

_____

_____

CONTRACTS

2

Contracts permeate the entire field of business law. You must, therefore, know the various kinds of contracts, the distinction between real and personal property, the definition of goods, and the essential elements of a contract. It is most important that the definition of "goods" be memorized and kept clearly in mind, because of the two sets of rules found in some of the chapters in Part 2, "Contracts."

Fill-in Questions. Write the correct word or words in the blank spaces to complete the following statements.

1. Contracts which are imposed by law to prevent injustice are known as _____ contracts.
2. A _____ contract lacks one or more of the essential elements of a contract.
3. An _____ contract may create an obligation, but such a contract cannot be enforced by legal proceedings.
4. An _____ contract denotes a contract which is yet to be performed.
5. A _____ contract is one in which one party receives as consideration for his promise the performance or forbearance of some act.
6. The terms of an _____ contract are stated by the parties.
7. The terms of a contract _____ are inferred from the acts of the parties.
8. A _____ contract is sometimes referred to as "a promise for a promise."
9. A _____ contract imposes on the contracting parties the same obligation as a valid contract unless the contract is rescinded.
10. A contract of record is a _____ contract.
11. A _____ contract contains all the essential elements of a contract.

12. The Commercial Code defines _____ as all things which are movable at the time of identification to the contract for sale.

True-False Questions. Indicate whether each of the following statements is true or false by circling the T or F.

T   *F*   1. The distinction between a sealed an an unsealed contract is highly important.

T   *F*   2. A contract entered into under duress is a void contract.

T   *F*   3. There is little distinction between a contract implied in fact and a contract implied in law.

T   *F*   4. Oral contracts which are required to be in writing are unenforceable.

T   *F*   5. Contracts under seal are classified as formal contracts.

Problems. Analyze each of the following factual situations and state your decision and the reason for your decision in the space provided.

1. On January 1, 1971, Brown entered into a contract with Jones whereby Brown agreed to sell Jones 200 typewriters on March 1, 1971. Brown contends that this is a contract for the sale of goods. Do you agree with this contention?

_____

_____

_____

_____

_____

2. Mary, who lost her diamond ring, placed an advertisement in a newspaper offering to pay a reward of $100 to anyone who found and returned the ring to her. Explain when a contractual relationship will be created.

_____

_____

_____

_____

_____

3. On February 1, 1971, Aaron entered into a contract with Allen whereby Aaron agreed to sell and Allen agreed to buy a certain lawnmower for $500. Assuming Allen did not pay for the lawnmower, explain whether Aaron would be permitted to bring an action to recover the $500 on February 1, 1978.

_____

_____

_____

_____

_____

_____

_____

_____

_____

_____

_____

4. Brown rented the upstairs floor of a restaurant to Jones for the purpose of carrying on an illegal business. Jones used the premises for two months without paying the rent. He then vacated the premises. Would Brown prevail in an action to collect the rent?

_____

_____

_____

_____

_____

_____

_____

_____

_____

5. What are the essential elements of a contract?

_____

_____

_____

_____

_____

_____

_____

CHAPTER 5
AGREEMENT

Chapter 5 explains the first essential element of a valid contract. This chapter, however, is one of the most important and one of the most difficult in the study of the law of contracts. You must learn when a valid offer has been made, when the offer has been terminated, and when the offer has been accepted. This chapter is also complicated by the two sets of rules. One set of rules pertains to contracts for services and real estate; the other set pertains to contracts for the sale of goods. You must, therefore, remember to answer problems pertaining to the sale of goods with the rules of law found in the Commercial Code.

Fill-in Questions. *Write the correct word or words in the blank spaces to complete the following statements.*

1. Additional or different terms in an acceptance do not necessarily prevent a contract for the sale of goods from being created provided both the offeror and the offeree are _____.
2. The offer, at an auction sale, is made by the _____.
3. An offer is not effective until it is properly _____ to the offeree.
4. A rejection is effective when it is received by the _____.
5. A revocation of an offer is effective when it is received by the _____.
6. An offer which is not revocable is known as an _____.
7. In reaching an agreement, it is the _____ of mutual assent that is important rather than the secret intention of the parties.
8. Quotations of a price of goods for sale which are published in newspapers are ordinarily invitations to _____.
9. An offer which limits the time for acceptance is sometimes referred to as a _____ offer.
10. The death or _____ of the offeror or offeree will terminate the offer.
11. A promise for an act is a _____ contract.
12. An irrevocable offer made by a merchant is known as a _____ offer.
13. An offer for the sale of goods may be accepted in any manner and by

any medium _____ in the circumstances unless a specific mode of acceptance is unambiguously indicated.

14. A _____, which is a reply in different terms to an offer made by the offeror, is made by the offeree.

True-False Questions. *Indicate whether each of the following statements is true or false by circling the T or F.*

T   *F*   1. Advertisements in newspapers are ordinarily invitations to make an offer.

T   *F*   2. An offer must always be in writing.

T   *F*   3. Persons who enter into social engagements are not thinking of legal obligations.

T   *F*   4. An offer must be communicated to the offeree.

T   *F*   5. The absence of literally definite terms in an offer will always render the contract indefinite.

T   *F*   6. An offer is never made irrevocable by statute.

T   *F*   7. A reply to an invitation to negotiate—an attempt to accept —is an offer only and will not create a contract unless, and until, it is accepted by the other party.

T   *F*   8. Silence on the part of the offeree will never constitute an acceptance.

T   *F*   9. Contracts for public works are not completed until the offer of the prospective contractor is accepted by some board or officer authorized to enter into contracts for public works.

T   *F*   10. Prior to acceptance of an offer, neither the offeror nor the offeree has obligated himself to the other party.

T   *F*   11. A reasonable time for accepting all offers is one month.

T   *F*   12. A counteroffer is made when the offeree replies to the offer stating that he desires to enter into a contract on terms different from those made by the offeror.

T   *F*   13. The acceptance of an offer by a reciprocal promise must be communicated to the offeror.

T   *F*   14. An acceptance of an offer deposited in the mail may be revoked by withdrawing the letter from the mail.

Problems. *Analyze each of the following factual situations and state your decision and the reason for your decision in the space provided.*

1. Butler, a shareholder in the XYZ Corporation, said to the general manager of the corporation: "You have been a very capable manager this past year. I am, therefore, going to divide my profits with you on a very liberal basis." The manager thanked Butler, but Butler failed to share the profits. Did Butler make an enforceable promise?

_____

_____

_____

_____

_____

_____

_____

_____

2. Cabot, a farmer, and The Hardware Company entered into a contract whereby Cabot promised to purchase from The Hardware Company, and The Hardware Company promised to sell and deliver to Cabot, five correctly described tractors on March 1. The Hardware Company delivered the tractors on March 1, and they were accepted by Cabot. Cabot refused, however, to pay the price requested by The Hardware Company. What remedy, if any, is available to The Hardware Company if no contract price had been previously agreed upon?

_____

_____

_____

_____

_____

_____

_____

_____

_____

_____

_____

3. An advertisement appeared in a newspaper notifying the public that Blackacre would be sold on November 28, 1970, at public auction. On the date stated, the auctioneer asked for bids from the assembled persons. Brown bid $10,000, there were no further bids, and the auc-

tioneer withdrew Blackacre from sale. Would Brown succeed in an action to compel the auctioneer to sell Blackacre to him for $10,000?

_____

_____

_____

_____

_____

_____

_____

4. Aaron wrote a letter to Adams offering to sell his farm to Adams for $10,000. Bob, an adult son of Adams, found the letter. Bob thereupon, in his own name, wrote Aaron a letter accepting the offer. Aaron, who then prepared a deed conveying the farm to Adams, went to the office of Adams for the purpose of completing the sale. Adams refused to purchase the farm. What remedy, if any, is available to Aaron?

_____

_____

_____

_____

_____

_____

5. Brown and Smith attended an auction sale for the purpose of purchasing a certain set of books. Brown bid $1,000, and Smith then bid $1,500 while the hammer was falling. (1) What are the rights of the auctioneer? (2) Suppose Smith was secretly the owner of the books. What are the rights of Brown?

_____

_____

_____

_____

_____

_____

_____

_____

6. Mary offered to sell her diamond ring to Jane for $500. About one year thereafter, Jane wrote a letter to Mary accepting the offer. Mary replied that she had recently sold the ring. Was Mary justified in selling the ring?

_____

_____

_____

_____

_____

7. The Cabinet Shop ordered by a written memorandum eight cabinets from Brown. The order stated: "I will pay the current market price if you will manufacture the cabinets according to my plans and specifications, which plans and specifications are enclosed." Brown, although he did not reply to the memorandum, did manufacture the cabinets and deliver them to The Cabinet Shop one year later. Is The Cabinet Shop obligated to accept the cabinets?

_____

_____

_____

_____

_____

_____

8. The seller, a manufacturer of hardwood doors, entered into a contract with the buyer, a building contractor, whereby the seller promised to sell all of the doors manufactured by him to the buyer, and the buyer promised to buy all the doors manufactured by the seller for a period of two years. At the time the contract was entered into, the seller manufactured approximately 200 doors per month. The seller, how-

ever, expanded his production to approximately 1,000 doors per month soon after the contract was entered into. Could the seller compel the buyer to accept the 1,000 doors per month?

_____

_____

_____

_____

_____

9. Baker sent Jones an offer by mail which was silent as to the time, manner, and mode of acceptance. Jones mailed a properly stamped and addressed letter of acceptance, which was destroyed as the result of a train accident and was not received by Baker. Is there a contract?

_____

_____

_____

_____

_____

_____

10. What is meant by the term "requirements and output contract"?

_____

_____

_____

_____

_____

_____

CHAPTER 6
CONSIDERATION

Chapter 6 explains the second essential element of a valid contract. You must learn the specific promises, acts, and forbearances that may or may not constitute consideration; the miscellaneous types of consideration that may or may not constitute sufficient consideration; and how claims may or may not be settled with or without consideration. Attention should be directed to the two sets of rules found in modification, rescission, and waiver.

Fill-in Questions. *Write the correct word or words in the blank spaces to complete the following statements.*

1. The _____ promises in a bilateral contract constitute the consideration.
2. A promise is supported by consideration if the _____ suffers a legal detriment.
3. The doctrine of equitable _____ holds that, as between two innocent parties, the one who makes the fraud possible must bear the loss resulting from such fraud.
4. An agreement by the parties to rescind a wholly executory contract is called mutual _____.
5. The term _____ consideration pertains to a promise founded on a natural duty of love and affection.
6. _____ estoppel is used when the promisee, relying on a gratuitous promise, suffers a detriment.
7. The word _____ is frequently defined as the voluntary relinquishment of a known right.
8. A _____ consideration is not sufficient to make a present promise enforceable.
9. A promise by a creditor to his debtor to discharge a _____ debt by the acceptance of a lesser sum is, without anything more, unenforceable.
10. As a general rule, the courts are not concerned with an _____ consideration.
11. Consideration is predicated on the idea that the _____ bargains for and receives something in exchange for his promise.
12. An _____ and _____ is the set-

tlement of a dispute or the satisfaction of a claim by means of a new executed contract between the parties.

13. A _____ and _____ is the settlement of an honestly disputed debt.

True-False Questions. Indicate whether each of the following statements is true or false by circling the T or F.

T   F   1. Actions must be brought on claims, including contracts for the payment of money, within a stated number of years to prevent the claim from being barred by the statute of limitations.

T   F   2. The courts have consistently held a composition with creditors to be binding.

T   F   3. Equitable estoppel is applied to the formation of contracts.

T   F   4. Courts frequently inquire into the adequacy of consideration when there is an exchange of goods of the same kind and quality at the same time and place.

T   F   5. Consideration must be sufficient in the sense that it has legal value in the eyes of the law.

T   F   6. A moral consideration is sufficient consideration for an executory promise.

T   F   7. All of the state legislatures have enacted statutes which provide that a promise to pay a debt barred by the statute of limitations must be in writing.

T   F   8. A surrender of the right to sue upon a claim is a sufficient consideration.

T   F   9. In a compromise and settlement, the surrender of the right to sue upon the claim constitutes consideration for a promise to settle for less.

T   F 10. A waiver after breach of contract requires consideration to be binding.

T   F 11. A promise made by a debtor to pay a debt which has been barred by a discharge in bankruptcy is enforceable without any new consideration.

Problems. Analyze each of the following factual situations and state your decision and the reason for your decision in the space provided.

1. Brown and Jones entered into an agreement whereby Brown agreed to buy certain land owned by Jones. As a part of the same agreement, Jones reserved the right to cancel the contract if he decided not to sell the land. Is this agreement enforceable by Jones?

_____

_____

2. Jan Baker went to Washington, D.C., on a sightseeing tour. He was unexpectedly taken ill, and Mr. and Mrs. Hull took him into their home where he was given medical aid and attention. After Jan Baker recovered and returned to his home, his father, upon learning of the services rendered to his son, promised Mr. and Mrs. Hull that he would pay them $1,000 and signed a promissory note for that sum. Will Jan Baker's father be required to pay this note?

3. Rogers agreed to construct and to complete by May 1 a garage for Barsh for the sum of $4,000. During the construction, Barsh said he would pay Rogers $100 as a bonus if Rogers would complete the garage by April 15. Rogers agreed and did finish the garage by April 15. Will Rogers be able to collect the $100?

4. Brown executed a writing in which he promised "for and in consideration of the love and affection I have for my son, Brown, Jr.," to convey Blackacre to Brown, Jr., when he returns home from the Vietnam war. Brown, Jr., returned home, and Brown conveyed Blackacre to him. Brown later changed his mind. He then asked the court to issue an order compelling Brown, Jr., to reconvey Blackacre to Brown. Decide.

5. The purchaser and seller entered into a contract for the purchase and sale of three specified patio doors for $300 each. They later agreed to modify the agreement by changing the price from $300 to $250 for each of the doors. Do you think this agreement to modify would be enforceable?

CHAPTER 7
CAPACITY OF PARTIES

Chapter 7 explains the third essential element of a valid contract. You must be able to identify those persons who have limited contractual capacity. This assertion will become obvious when it is learned that many competent persons enter into contracts with incapacitated persons and later learn that the contract has been disaffirmed. It is important to concentrate on the rights given incapacitated persons and the liabilities imposed upon them. The fact that Chapter 7 is devoted principally to infants does not mean that contracts of other incapacitated persons deserve less attention.

Fill-in Questions. *Write the correct word or words in the blank spaces to complete the following statements.*

1. The _____ of a contract by an infant is a manifestation of an intent not to perform.

2. An infant may be held liable in quasi contract for the reasonable value of the _____ furnished him.

3. A contract entered into by an infant cannot be ratified by the infant until he attains his _____ or a reasonable time thereafter.

4. A parent is not liable for the _____ acts of his minor child merely because of parental reasons.

5. The vast majority of the contracts entered into by an infant are _____.

6. An infant cannot disaffirm a sale of _____ until he reaches his majority.

7. Contracts of an insane or mentally _____ person are generally voidable.

8. A parent is entitled to any compensation which the infant earns unless the infant is _____.

9. The guardian of judicially declared insane persons may _____ or _____ previously made agreements by the incompetent.

10. The _____ of a contract by an infant is a manifestation to perform.

True-False Questions. Indicate whether each of the following statements is true or false by circling the T or F.

T   *F*   1. Emancipation of an infant by the infant's parents must be in writing and witnessed by two persons.

T   *F*   2. As a general rule, any words or acts by an infant which clearly indicate an intent to repudiate a contract will operate as a disaffirmance.

T   *F*   3. An infant who misrepresents his age and thereby induces an adult to enter into a contract may never be held liable for the tort of deceit.

T   *F*   4. Continued silence on the part of an infant upon reaching his majority would indicate an intent to ratify a wholly executed contract.

T   *F*   5. In all of the states, the disability of nonage has been removed for all persons aged eighteen or over.

T   *F*   6. As a general rule, an infant tort-feasor is liable in a civil action to the injured person to the same extent as an adult.

T   *F*   7. Contracts of insane or mentally incompetent persons are generally valid.

T   *F*   8. Contracts of intoxicated persons are void.

Problems. Analyze each of the following factual situations and state your decision and the reason for your decision in the space provided.

1. Taylor purchased a motorcycle from Barsh, an infant. Taylor thereafter resold the motorcycle to Black, a good faith purchaser. Barsh, while still an infant, decided that he wanted his motorcycle. He thereupon offered to return the money he received for the motorcycle to Black, and demanded the return of his motorcycle. Will Barsh succeed?

_____

_____

_____

_____

_____

_____

_____

_____

_____

2. An infant, in order to raise funds to complete his education, sold some land to Brown for a fair price. Soon after the infant reached his majority, he learned that he could get a better price from Jones. The infant therefore tendered back the purchase price to Brown and demanded the return of the land. Brown refused to comply with this request. The infant nevertheless sold the land to Jones. Would Jones succeed in an action against Brown to get possession of the land?

_____

_____

_____

_____

_____

_____

_____

_____

_____

3. An infant purchased certain goods that would ordinarily be classed as necessaries for his station in life. The seller brought an action against the infant's guardian for the reasonable value of the goods. It was proved at the trial that the infant was abundantly supplied with this class of goods. Decide.

_____

_____

_____

_____

_____

_____

_____

_____

4. An infant, while driving an automobile, struck and severely injured a pedestrian. The injured pedestrian brought an action for damages. At the trial it was shown that the infant had passed a red light at the street intersection just before striking the pedestrian. The infant attempted to escape liability on the ground that he was a minor. Decide.

5. Staley, twenty years of age, rented an apartment from Abel for nine months. He planned to live in the apartment while enrolled at State University. He lived in the apartment for three months and paid the rent, whereupon he moved to another apartment. Does Staley have any liability to Abel for the last six months under the lease?

CHAPTER 8
ILLEGALITY

Chapter 8 explains the fourth and last essential element of a valid contract. You must learn to distinguish between a contract that is illegal and a contract that is not illegal; the remedies for illegality; and the rule of in pari delicto. It must be kept in mind that most contracts which are illegal in one state are also illegal in other states, but that it is possible for a contract to be legal in one state and illegal in another.

Fill-in Questions. *Write the correct word or words in the blank spaces to complete the following statements.*

1. Sunday laws are known as _____ laws.
2. The charging of a higher rate of interest than is allowed by statute is known as _____.
3. A contract which amounts to a partial restraint of trade is enforceable, provided the restraint is _____ to the contract and is reasonable.
4. The courts will not give relief to parties to an illegal contract where they are in _____ or equally at fault.
5. A contract to _____ trade cannot be enforced when the sole purpose of the agreement is to eliminate competition.
6. The Federal Consumer Credit Protection Act is commonly known as the _____ Act.
7. A contract which is based upon the determination of an uncertain event is a _____ and is generally illegal.
8. The legal part of a partly illegal contract is enforceable if the contract is _____.

True-False Questions. *Indicate whether each of the following statements is true or false by circling the T or F.*

T   F   1. An insurance contract in which the insured has no interest in the property insured at the time the contract is made is legal.

T   F   2. The rule "an agreement which has for its object the commission of a civil wrong is illegal" is limited to statutory wrongs.

T   *F*   3.   An agreement which is illegal in one state is illegal in all the other states.

T   *F*   4.   Wagering contracts, such as raffles and door prizes, are often approved when used to raise money for a charitable purpose.

T   *F*   5.   A contract to monopolize trade cannot be enforced when the sole purpose of the agreement is to eliminate the competition.

T   *F*   6.   The legal rate of interest provided by the statutes of the various states is the maximum rate.

Problems. *Analyze each of the following factual situations and state your decision and the reason for your decision in the space provided.*

1. Baker, Jr., who was an accountant, falsely told his elderly father, Baker, Sr., who owed certain debts, that his creditors were filing proceedings in court to take his assets. Baker, Jr., thereby induced his father to transfer all his assets to him. Do you think Baker, Sr., could have the transfer set aside?

_____

_____

_____

_____

_____

_____

_____

_____

_____

2. Brown purchased merchandise from The Department Store in the amount of $600, and promised to pay for the merchandise in six monthly installments. The Department Store contended that this sale was not subject to the Federal Consumer Credit Protection Act because the sale was an intrastate transaction. Do you agree with this contention?

_____

_____

_____

_____

_____

_____

_____

_____

_____

_____

3. Brown, who delivered merchandise for The Acme Company, was given a package to deliver to Jones. Brown was instructed to "deliver this package" to Jones. When Brown was in the process of delivering the package, it was confiscated by police officers. The package contained heroin, and Brown was arrested. Does Brown have a cause of action against The Acme Company to collect his fee for this delivery?

_____

_____

_____

_____

_____

_____

_____

_____

_____

_____

4. Taylor, an officer of the X Bank, borrowed $5,000 from the bank at a usurious rate of interest. Will the X Bank be able to recover the money from Taylor if he asserts the defense of illegality as an excuse for not repaying the loan?

_____

_____

_____

_____

_____

CHAPTER 9
REALITY OF CONSENT

Let it be assumed that Brown and Jones, both of whom have capacity to contract, have entered into a contract (1) by an offer and acceptance, (2) supported by sufficient consideration, (3) the object of which is legal. It is nevertheless possible that either Brown or Jones may rescind the contract or they may bring an action for damages based upon fraud. The aim of Chapter 9 is to explain (1) when the contract may be avoided on the ground that there was not real consent and (2) when an action for damages may be brought.

Fill-in Questions. *Write the correct word or words in the blank spaces to complete the following statements.*

1. _____ or nondisclosure in and of itself is not a misrepresentation in the absence of a duty to speak.
2. Actionable fraud entitles a person to bring an action for damages based upon fraud and is called an action for _____.
3. An expression of _____ is known as dealers' talk.
4. A threat to prosecute a criminal action against a relative will constitute _____.
5. The Code provides that the court may refuse to enforce a contract where an _____ advantage has been taken of one of the parties.
6. A mistake is _____ when it is entertained by both the contracting parties.
7. The essence of undue _____ is the mental coercion of one person over another.
8. The opinion of an _____ is treated as a statement of fact.
9. A mistake is _____ if only one of the parties entertains an erroneous belief.
10. The plaintiff must prove _____ in an action for deceit.

True-False Questions. *Indicate whether each of the following statements is true or false by circling the T or F.*

T   F   1. The mistake of a scrivener in reducing an agreement to writing may not be reformed.

T	*F*	2.	A mutual mistake may prevent the existence of a contract.
T	*F*	3.	In an action for deceit, the plaintiff must prove that the defendant made the representation knowing at the time that it was false.
T	*F*	4.	A statement that an article cost so much is one of opinion.
T	*F*	5.	The gist of silence as constituting misrepresentation is the producing of a false impression upon the mind of another person.
T	*F*	6.	A false representation is a misrepresentation which may be made by words, writings, or conduct.
T	*F*	7.	Pecuniary damages are not recoverable for a misstatement of a material fact unaccompanied by fraud.
T	*F*	8.	Duress is the only one of the possible causes of unreality of consent which gives a remedy not only of rescission but also of an action in tort for damages.
T	*F*	9.	A person who occupies a fiduciary relationship to another person is required to disclose all information which is material to the particular transaction.
T	*F*	10.	A contracting party will not be permitted to rescind the contract where both parties are merely ignorant as to the value of the subject matter.

Problems. Analyze each of the following factual situations and state your decision and the reason for your decision in the space provided.

1. Brown, who offered to sell Jones Lot 12 in an undeveloped subdivision for $1,000, told Jones he was willing to sell at this low price because he needed the cash. Brown also told Jones that he had secretly learned that the subdivision was going to be developed within six months. Jones did not believe the statements of Brown were true, but Jones purchased Lot 12 because he thought it was a good investment. The subdivision was not developed, and Jones sold Lot 12 for $250. Would Jones recover in an action against Brown for fraud?

_____

_____

_____

_____

_____

_____

_____

2. Mary, who was twenty-one years of age, consistently sought the advice of her domineering brother about the money she had inherited from her uncle. Mary and her brother went to the First Bank, and her brother induced her to sign an agreement which provided that if the bank would lend the brother $10,000 she would pay the loan if he failed to do so. The officers of the bank knew that Mary relied on the domineering brother and also heard him induce her to sign the agreement. Would the First Bank prevail in an action to recover the $10,000 from Mary if the brother failed to repay the $10,000?

_____

_____

_____

_____

_____

_____

_____

3. Brown installed an air-conditioning system for Jones. The system did not operate satisfactorily, and Jones refused to pay the purchase price. Brown, in good faith, then promised Jones that he would remedy all the deficiencies if Jones would pay the purchase price. Jones paid the purchase price, but Brown did not remedy the deficiencies. Jones brought an action in tort against Brown to recover damages for deceit. Should he recover?

_____

_____

_____

_____

_____

_____

_____

4. A contractor asked Roberts at what price he would sell certain machinery. Roberts agreed to sell the machinery for $1,150, which price seemed reasonable to the contractor, who agreed to accept the machinery. The machinery was delivered and accepted. Roberts thereafter billed the contractor for $1,250, claiming that he had made a mistake in computing the price. Can Roberts recover the additional $100?

_____

_____

_____

_____

_____

_____

_____

_____

5. Cabot, a real estate broker, showed Davis a certain tract of land which Cabot stated belonged to Smith. It was later learned that the land was not the land which Smith intended to sell. Davis brought an action to have the contract rescinded, and Cabot contended that he had acted in good faith and had honestly believed the land shown to Davis to be the tract of land Smith proposed to sell, and that the contract could not be rescinded. Do you agree with this contention?

_____

_____

_____

_____

_____

_____

_____

_____

CHAPTER 10
CONTRACTS REQUIRED
TO BE IN WRITING

Contracting parties may enter into a contract valid in all respects, and then learn that the contract is not enforceable in court. The important points for you to remember, therefore, are the expressions "within the Statute of Frauds" and "without the Statute of Frauds." The expression "within the Statute of Frauds" means that the contract cannot be enforced in court unless the contract is in writing or there is an acceptable substitute for the writing. The expression "without the Statute of Frauds" means that an oral contract is enforceable in court. Chapter 10 explains the various classes of contracts that are required to be in writing; the provisions of the Code which provide that a contract for the sale of goods for the price of $500 or more is not enforceable in court unless it is evidenced by some writing; and the acceptable substitutes to a writing.

Fill-in Questions. *Write the correct word or words in the blank spaces to complete the following statements.*

1. A promise to answer for the debt of another is in the nature of a _____.

2. A _____ or _____ promise to pay for the debt of another is required to be in writing.

3. An employee who has rendered services to an employer in reliance on a contract unenforceable because of the Statute of Frauds may recover on a _____ contract.

4. Provision is made by the Code for the enforceability of oral contracts where the goods are to be made _____ for the buyer.

5. The Code specifically provides that the contract is not enforceable beyond the _____ of goods shown in the memorandum.

6. A special promise by an executor to pay the debts of the decedent out of the assets of the estate of the _____ is required to be in writing.

7. Mutual promises to _____, or engagement contracts, are without the Statute of Frauds.

8. Contracts which cannot be performed within a _____ from the date they are entered into are within the Statute of Frauds.
9. The Statute of Frauds does not require that the contract be reduced to a _____ written document.
10. An example of a guaranty of _____ is created when Cabot calls Baker by telephone and states: "Sell groceries not exceeding $100 to Abel, try to collect from him, but if you cannot, I will pay you."

True-False Questions. Indicate whether each of the following statements is true or false by circling the T or F.

T   *F*   1. Modification or rescission includes abandonment or other change by mutual consent.

T   *F*   2. An oral promise, the effect of which is to incur a joint debt with another person, is not enforceable.

T   *F*   3. There is no distinction between the expressions "payment guaranteed" and "collection guaranteed" in promises to answer for the debt of another.

T   *F*   4. A contract whereby money is lent but, by the terms of the agreement, repayment thereof is extended by installments beyond a one-year period is without the Statute of Frauds.

T   *F*   5. A contract of employment to act as the broker for the sale and purchase of real property is within the Statute of Frauds.

T   *F*   6. In promises to answer for the debt of another, the guarantor is liable only if the other person fails to perform.

T   *F*   7. An oral agreement for the sale of land is generally enforceable if there has been a part performance.

T   *F*   8. In promises to answer for the debt of another, a promise made to the debtor which is based upon sufficient consideration is without the Statute of Frauds.

T   *F*   9. A contract for a period of time longer than one year after the contract is made, even though performance is to begin in the future, is within the Statute of Frauds.

T   *F*   10. A contract to give one employment for as long as he lives is without the Statute of Frauds.

Problems. Analyze each of the following factual situations and state your decision and the reason for your decision in the space provided.

1. The seller and the buyer, both merchants, entered into an oral contract for the purchase and sale of certain goods for the amount of $5,000. The seller immediately mailed the buyer a written confirma-

tion of the sale. How could the buyer prevent the seller from enforcing the oral contract?

_____

_____

_____

_____

_____

2. Baker, a merchant, employed Brown as a clerk for a period of eighteen months at a stated salary. Baker reduced the terms of the agreement to writing, signed the document and gave it to Brown, who has since retained its possession. Brown worked for two months and without just cause quit the employment of Baker. Will Baker succeed if he sues Brown for breach of contract?

_____

_____

_____

_____

_____

_____

_____

3. Same facts as problem 2 above except that Baker without just cause dismissed Brown from his employment. Can Brown recover damages from Baker for breach of contract?

_____

_____

_____

_____

_____

4. Brown and Smith entered into an oral contract for the purchase and sale of certain goods for the amount of $5,000. Smith admitted in his

testimony that he entered into a contract but contended that the amount was only $4,500 and that the oral contract was unenforceable because of the Statute of Frauds. Do you agree with this contention?

_____

_____

_____

_____

_____

_____

5. Taylor sold his store to Brown for $75,000. Brown orally promised, as a part of the same transaction, that he would pay $5,000 to the X Wholesale Company—a debt which Taylor owed the company. After the sale was consummated, Brown refused to pay the X Wholesale Company. Was Brown's promise to pay this debt of $5,000 required to be in writing?

_____

_____

_____

_____

_____

_____

6. Cabot was in possession of and operating a clothing store which belonged to Davis. The store was encumbered by a first mortgage in favor of Smith and a second mortgage in favor of Cabot. Smith threatened to foreclose the mortgage, and Cabot orally promised to pay the first mortgage indebtedness if Smith would not foreclose. Cabot contends his oral promise is not enforceable because of the Statute of Frauds. Decide.

_____

_____

_____

_____

_____

_____

CHAPTER 11
RIGHTS OF
THIRD PARTIES

Chapter 11 is devoted to the rights and duties of third-party beneficiaries and assignees. A beneficiary and an assignee of a contract are similar in that neither is an original contracting party. You must remember, however, that the rights and duties of beneficiaries and assignees are quite dissimilar.

Fill-in Questions. Write the correct word or words in the blank spaces to complete the following statements.

1. A third party for whose benefit a contract is made is known as a _____.

2. A contract made for the benefit of a third person who is a creditor of the promisee is a _____ beneficiary.

3. An assignor impliedly _____ that he will do nothing to impede or prevent collection of the debt by the assignee.

4. An _____ beneficiary is a person who happens to be benefitted by a contract which is made primarily for the benefit of the parties to the contract.

5. As a general rule, an _____ and a beneficiary are permitted to sue upon a contract entered into by third persons.

6. An assignee should give _____ of the assignment to the obligor-debtor in order to establish his claim.

7. When there are successive assignees to the same right, it is generally held that the assignee with the prior right is the one who _____ gives notice.

8. Contracts for _____ are not assignable.

9. The assignment of a contract transfers the _____ subject to the _____.

10. A donee beneficiary, when he is permitted to sue on the contract made for his benefit, is permitted to sue only the _____.

True-False Questions. Indicate whether each of the following statements is true or false by circling the T or F.

T　　*F*　　1. The usual life insurance policy is a good example of a donee beneficiary contract.

T	F	2.	The absence of consideration in an assignment may defeat a claim in contracts between assignees.
T	F	3.	Future earnings of a person under a contract of employment may not be assigned.
T	F	4.	There is no distinction between the rights and duties of a third-party beneficiary and an assignee of a contract.
T	F	5.	As assignee should give the debtor notice of the assignment.
T	F	6.	An assignor impliedly warrants that the debtor will pay the debt.
T	F	7.	An assignee takes the debt subject to all the defenses which the debtor may have had against the assignor at the time of the assignment and arising thereafter prior to notice of the assignment.
T	F	8.	The Code recognizes that both delegation of performance and assignment of rights are normal incidents of a contract for the sale of goods.

Problems. *Analyze each of the following factual situations and state your decision and the reason for your decision in the space provided.*

1. A contract contained a clause which prohibited the assignment of "the contract." What would be the effect of this clause under the Code?

_____

_____

_____

_____

_____

_____

_____

_____

2. Brown, who had entered into a contract with Jones, assigned "all my rights under the contract" to Smith. How would this assignment be construed under the Code?

_____

_____

_____

_____

_____

_____

3. Mr. Baker insured his life for $10,000 and named his son as the beneficiary. He was not, however, indebted to his son. Mr. Baker died. Does his son have the right to collect the proceeds of the insurance policy?

_____

_____

_____

_____

_____

_____

_____

_____

_____

4. Jones made arrangements with the First Bank to borrow $5,000 but before the money was actually lent transferred to Kelley his right to borrow the money. Kelley contends that the First Bank is under a duty to lend the $5,000 to him. Is he correct?

_____

_____

_____

_____

_____

_____

_____

_____

_____

_____

5. Brown purchased certain furniture from Jones for $10,000, for which he agreed to pay in thirty days. Brown then sold the furniture to Smith, who promised to pay Jones. Jones, in reliance on the promise of Smith, borrowed $8,000 from the First Bank. Do you think Brown and Smith have a right to rescind their agreement?

_____

_____

_____

_____

_____

_____

_____

_____

_____

_____

_____

_____

CHAPTER 12
PERFORMANCE

Chapter 12 explains conditions in contracts and performance of contracts. You must learn the various classes of conditions, and it is important to keep in mind that the breach of a condition precedent is a material breach and justifies the innocent party in rescinding the contract. How is one to determine if a breach is the breach of a condition precedent? If the objective of the contract is made impossible to achieve by such a breach, it is a breach of a condition precedent. It is also important to keep in mind the distinction between the doctrine of substantial performance and partial performance. The remedies under the two doctrines are entirely different. You should also keep in mind the distinction between "personal satisfaction" and "performance as would satisfy a reasonable man" when satisfaction is made a condition.

Fill-in Questions. *Write the correct word or words in the blank spaces to complete the following statements.*

1. A clause in a contract which requires that both parties are to act simultaneously is called a condition _____.

2. _____ performance accompanied by good faith is all that is required in order to entitle a person to recover on the contract.

3. A clause in a contract which calls for the performance of some act before there is a duty of immediate performance of the promise which is so conditioned is a condition _____.

4. The expression "time is of the _____" is frequently used to indicate that a condition precedent is intended.

5. The doctrine of substantial preformance must be clearly distinguished from _____ performance.

6. The term "entire contract" is used to mean an _____ contract as distinguished from a _____ contract.

7. When the continued existence of a _____ thing is essential to the performance of a contract, the destruction of the thing will terminate the contract.

8. A clause in a contract which gives one of the parties the option of treating the contract as discharged upon the breach of a condition is a condition _____.

True-False Questions. Indicate whether each of the following statements is true or false by circling the T or F.

T   *F*   1. An entire contract is one in which there is only one agreement covering all of the terms.

T   *F*   2. Impossibility created by unavoidable accident will always discharge the contract.

T   *F*   3. There is no distinction between the frustration of a contract and the termination of a contract.

T   *F*   4. A promise expressly conditioned upon the approval of some third person is frequently found in building contracts.

T   *F*   5. A typical illustration of a condition subsequent is found in an insurance policy which provides that the insured shall give the insurer notice of loss by fire within a specified time.

T   *F*   6. Performance of a part of an entire contract, as a general rule, imposes no immediate duty on the other party to perform.

T   *F*   7. Conditions are classified with regard to their function as conditions subsequent, concurrent, and precedent.

T   *F*   8. A typical illustration of a condition precedent is found in contracts of sale where payment and delivery are to be contemporaneous.

T   *F*   9. Recovery is always allowed on a quasi contract where a person partially performs an entire contract.

Problems. Analyze each of the following factual situations and state your decision and the reason for your decision in the space provided.

1. Brown was very eager to have his photograph made for the purpose of giving it to his girl friend. He contracted with a photographer to make the photograph to the entire satisfaction of Brown. After the photograph was made and delivered to Brown, he did not like it. Does the photographer have a cause of action against Brown for the contract price?

_____

_____

_____

_____

_____

_____

2. On July 1, Baker contracted to sell his horse "Prince" to Brown for $6,000. Brown paid the money to Baker, and they both immediately went to the stable so that Brown could take delivery of his horse. It was then learned that "Prince" had been killed by lightning during a severe storm at about 9 P.M. on June 30. Is Brown correct when he insists that Baker will have to refund the purchase price?

_____

_____

_____

_____

_____

_____

_____

_____

3. Davis, who entered into a contract with Drake to construct a duplex apartment, subcontracted the painting of the apartment to Jones. The contract between Davis and Jones provided that payment would be made to Jones when payment was received by Davis from Drake. The apartment was completed, but Drake failed to pay Davis. Would Jones recover in an action against Davis to recover the contract price of the painting?

_____

_____

_____

_____

_____

_____

_____

_____

_____

4. Drake agreed to construct and have completed by April 1 a swimming pool for Moore in the rear of Moore's house. The pool was not completed until April 10, and Moore refused to pay Drake. Did the failure of Drake to finish the pool on the date specified release Moore from liability?

_____

_____

_____

_____

_____

_____

_____

_____

5. Brown, who was employed by The Transit Company, was injured in an accident. As a part of the settlement with Brown for his injuries, The Transit Company promised Brown a lifetime free pass on its buses. Shortly thereafter, the state legislature enacted a statute forbidding any transit company from issuing free passes. Brown then brought an action against The Transit Company for damages for failure to perform by issuing the agreed free pass. Should he recover?

_____

_____

_____

_____

_____

_____

_____

_____

_____

_____

CHAPTER 13
REMEDIES, DAMAGES, INTERPRETATION

What remedies are available to the injured party for breach of contract? The answer to the question is found, for the most part, in this chapter. It is important to remember that a person who elects to rescind the contract cannot thereafter maintain an action for damages for the breach, but in a sale of goods the aggrieved party who rescinds does not thereby lose his right to damages. It is also important to keep in mind the distinction between mandatory and negative injunction. You must (1) be able to distinguish the various types of damages, (2) know what evidence is excluded and what evidence is admissible under the parol-evidence rule, (3) learn the primary and secondary rules in the construction of contracts, and (4) know the liability of persons in joint and several contracts.

Fill-in Questions. *Write the correct word or words in the blank spaces to complete the following statements.*

1. The _____ of a contract is the process of ascertaining the intention of the makers of the contract.
2. A _____ of a contract puts an end to the contract and puts the parties, insofar as possible, back in the same position they were in prior to the making of the contract.
3. _____ is a remedy whereby a person is required to do precisely what he ought to have done under the terms of the contract.
4. The remedy for preventing a person from doing some act is known as an _____ .
5. The rules of construction of contracts are ordinarily classified as _____ and _____ rules.
6. The courts will enforce a provision for liquidated damages but will not enforce a provision which is actually a _____ although it is called liquidated damages by the terms of the contract.
7. Evidence of fraud, duress, undue influence, and subsequent oral agreements is not excluded by the _____ rule.
8. Parties are prevented from introducing evidence during the trial of a case of _____ or _____

oral agreements which would vary or contradict a completely written contract by the parol-evidence rule.

9. Trifling sums awarded as a result of a breach of contract are known as _____ damages.

10. Damages that are traceable to and are the probable and necessary result of the injury are known as _____ damages.

11. In the construction of contracts, _____ words will govern if there is a conflict between the printed and written words.

True-False Questions. Indicate whether each of the following statements is true or false by circling the T or F.

T   *F*   1. The parol-evidence rule excludes evidence of prior or contemporaneous oral agreements which would vary the completely written contract.

T   *F*   2. As a general rule, a person is limited in his recovery for breach of contract to the loss he has actually suffered because of the breach.

T   *F*   3. A discharge of one joint obligor, as by an accord and satisfaction, generally does not discharge the remaining joint obligors.

T   *F*   4. In the construction of contracts, obvious mistakes of grammar will not be corrected.

T   *F*   5. It is generally held to be the duty of a discharged employee to obtain other employment of a like nature in the same locality.

T   *F*   6. Parol evidence is not admissible to identify persons mentioned in the contract.

T   *F*   7. An affirmative injunction commands a person to do some particular act.

T   *F*   8. The Code provides that a negotiable instrument which is signed by two or more persons as makers creates a joint liability.

Problems. Analyze each of the following factual situations and state your decision and the reason for your decision in the space provided.

1. A soup company agreed to purchase from defendant all the red-cored carrots grown on certain land at a price of $100. When the carrots matured, the market price of the carrots so grown was $300. The defendant refused to deliver the carrots to the soup company. Red-cored carrots were unobtainable elsewhere. Can the soup company obtain a decree of specific performance against the defendant?

2. A manufacturer and a dealer entered into a contract whereby the manufacturer agreed to manufacture certain kitchen cabinets for the dealer. The manufacturer was approximately one-half finished with the cabinets when the dealer repudiated the contract. What remedy, or remedies, are available to the manufacturer?

3. Davis induced Brown to purchase a horse for $1,500 by stating that the horse had no disease. Davis knew, however, that the horse was suffering from a latent illness which would result in the death of the horse in several months. Two weeks after the sale, Brown learned of the illness of the horse. Can Brown recover the $1,500?

4. Smith employed Davis as a clerk at $100 a week for one year. Without just cause, Davis quit the employment of Smith at the end of seven months and began to work for Marcus, a competitor of Smith. Do you think that Smith can get a decree of specific performance and force Davis to work the remaining five months?

_____

_____

_____

_____

_____

_____

_____

_____

_____

5. On January 10, Adams agreed in writing to sell Baker a certain harvester for $1,200 and deliver it on or before July 1 of the same year for the purpose of harvesting the wheat grown by Baker. Adams failed to deliver on July 1, and on July 14 Baker was able to purchase the same type of harvester from Cabot for $1,400. In the meantime, the wheat belonging to Baker had deteriorated to the extent of $10,000. Discuss the rights of Baker to recover from Adams the extra expenditure of $200 and the $10,000.

_____

_____

_____

_____

_____

_____

_____

_____

CHAPTER 14
DISCHARGE OF CONTRACTS

What should you get out of Chapter 14? At least, (1) the rules pertaining to part payment and tender of payment, (2) the remedies available to an injured party for breach of contract, (3) how a contract may be discharged by operation of law, (4) the methods by which a contract may be discharged by substituted agreement and alteration, and (5) the two general classes of arbitration.

Fill-in Questions. *Write the correct word or words in the blank spaces to complete the following statements.*

1. The substitution of a new party for one of the original contracting parties is a common example of a _____.

2. A valid _____ of payment discharges all liens, and interest no longer accrues.

3. A _____ of contract occurs when one of the contracting parties fails to perform an immediate duty under the contract.

4. An _____ breach occurs when one of the contracting parties announces, before the time for performance arrives, that he will not perform.

5. The period of the statute of _____ begins to run as soon as the cause of action accrues.

6. A discharge in _____ releases the debtor from all his debts which are provable in bankruptcy.

7. A judgment recovered in an action for breach of contract discharges by _____ the right of action arising from the breach.

8. A monthly statement of a bank of its depositors is a familiar example of an _____.

9. _____ is a method by which differences may be settled voluntarily without court action.

10. A _____ never to sue by a creditor is effective as an agreement not to enforce an existing cause of action.

11. An arbitration agreement may be a _____ agreement or an agreement to _____.

True-False Questions. Indicate whether each of the following statements is true or false by circling the T or F.

T   *F*   1. Bankruptcy is a method whereby a contract for the payment of a debt may be discharged by operation of law.

T   *F*   2. Agreements to arbitrate existing disputes are always revocable.

T   *F*   3. A partial breach of contract permits the injured party to bring an action for damages and recover for the partial breach.

T   *F*   4. The courts tend to treat a willful failure to perform as a material breach.

T   *F*   5. A debtor is never released from a contract for the payment of his debts by statutory enactments.

T   *F*   6. If neither the debtor nor the creditor makes an application of a payment when the debtor owes the creditor several accounts, the payment will be credited to a prior matured debt.

T   *F*   7. An account stated is an unliquidated debt.

T   *F*   8. The debtor must remain ready, willing, and able to pay the debt at any time in order to keep a tender valid.

Problems. Analyze each of the following factual situations and state your decision and the reason for your decision in the space provided.

1. Brown, who purchased certain merchandise from a department store, owed the store $500 on an open account for the merchandise. The store brought an action against Brown to recover the $500, and was awarded a judgment for that amount. The store thereafter attempted to collect the $500 on the open account. Will the store recover?

_____

_____

_____

_____

_____

_____

_____

_____

2. Plaintiff, who was the holder and owner of a promissory note for $200 signed by defendant as maker, fraudulently changed the amount of the note to $1,200. Plaintiff then brought an action against defendant to recover the $1,200. What defense, if any, is available to defendant?

_____

_____

_____

_____

_____

_____

_____

_____

_____

_____

3. Baker and Hipp were jointly liable on a debt for $2,000 to Taylor. By a written agreement, Taylor covenanted never to sue Baker on the debt. Taylor thereafter brought an action against Baker and Hipp to recover the $2,000. Baker pleaded the covenant as a defense. Is this a good defense?

_____

_____

_____

_____

_____

_____

_____

_____

_____

_____

4. Brown and Jones entered into a contract by the terms of which Brown agreed to sell and Jones agreed to buy Blackacre on January 1, 1971, for $30,000. On December 10, 1970, Jones wrote a letter to Brown stating that he (Jones) would not perform by purchasing Blackacre. Brown did not answer the letter. On January 1, 1971, Jones tendered the $30,000, but Brown refused to perform. Should Jones recover in an action for breach of contract?

_____

_____

_____

_____

_____

_____

_____

_____

_____

_____

_____

SALES

3

CHAPTER 15
SALES: INTRODUCTION

Chapter 15 and the next three chapters, which are devoted to the sale of goods, are governed by the Uniform Commercial Code. The rules of law are not difficult, but the chapters are comprehensive. This chapter gives a detailed definition of "goods," which must be memorized. You must also understand the rules in this chapter, or the rules in the remaining three chapters will not be easy to comprehend.

Fill-in Questions. *Write the correct word or words in the blank spaces to complete the following statements.*

1. The Code defines _____ as all things which are movable at the time of identification to the contract for sale.
2. Goods which are neither existing nor identified are known as _____ goods.
3. Common examples of _____ goods are grains and liquids.
4. Shipments by carrier contemplates a _____ contract or a _____ contract.
5. The delivery term _____ means collect on delivery, _____ means free on board, _____ means alongside at a named port, and _____ means cost, insurance, and freight.
6. The innocent purchaser for value has a superior right when he purchases from a merchant as opposed to one who _____ merchandise to a merchant.
7. A transaction is a _____ where the goods are delivered to the buyer primarily for a resale.
8. A transaction is a _____ where the goods are delivered to the buyer primarily for use.
9. A buyer in the _____ is one who buys in the ordinary course from a person in the business of selling goods of that kind and who buys in good faith and without knowledge that the sale to him is in violation of the ownership rights or security interest of a third person in the goods.

True-False Questions. Indicate whether each of the following statements is true or false by circling the T or F.

T   F   1. An attempted present sale of future goods operates as a contract to sell.

T   F   2. The definition of "goods" includes specially manufactured goods.

T   F   3. Article 2, "Sales," of the Code applies to both the transfer of personal property and the transfer of realty.

T   F   4. Shipping goods f.a.s. vessel merely reserves to the seller control over the possession of the goods until payment.

T   F   5. Title passes from the seller to the buyer on tender of delivery at the place of shipment in a shipment contract.

T   F   6. Title passes from the seller to the buyer when the seller delivers the document if the seller is required to deliver a document.

T   F   7. A merchant who is entrusted with goods of the kind which he sells is clothed with power to transfer all of the rights of the entruster-owner to a buyer in the ordinary course of business.

T   F   8. One who buys from a merchant whose inventory is being financed is not a buyer in the ordinary course of business.

T   F   9. The bulk sales law does not include those who manufacture what they sell.

T   F   10. In a bulk sale, the transferee must file a list of creditors and schedule of the property with some designated state official.

T   F   11. The creditors in a bulk sale, as a general rule, must look to the proceeds of the sale.

T   F   12. A sale or a contract to sell must always be in writing.

T   F   13. Goods to be specially manufactured and not suitable for sale to others are held to be without the Statute of Frauds.

Problems. Analyze each of the following factual situations and state your decision and the reason for your decision in the space provided.

1. Brown, in Jacksonville, Florida, ordered certain goods from a dealer, in Detroit, Michigan. The goods were to be shipped f.o.b. Jacksonville, Florida. Is the risk of loss on Brown or on the dealer during transportation from Detroit to Jacksonville?

_____

_____

_____

_____

_____

_____

_____

_____

2. Would your answer be the same in problem 1 if the goods were to be shipped f.o.b. Detroit, Michigan?

_____

_____

_____

_____

_____

_____

_____

3. Brown purchased a specific executive desk from defendant, an office supply company, for $1,000 on Monday morning and paid cash in advance. The defendant agreed to deliver the desk on Wednesday. On Tuesday, the creditors of the defendant attached all of the inventory of defendant, including the desk which had been sold to Brown. Is Brown or are the creditors entitled to the desk?

_____

_____

_____

_____

_____

_____

_____

_____

4. Brown, a farmer, had 300 bushels of corn of the same grade and quality stored in a public warehouse. He sold 100 bushels of the corn to Jones and 200 bushels to Smith and delivered to each a negotiable warehouse receipt. The public warehouse was thereafter destroyed by fire. Who must stand the loss?

_____

_____

_____

_____

_____

_____

_____

_____

_____

_____

5. What is the purpose of the bulk sales statutes?

_____

_____

_____

_____

_____

_____

_____

_____

_____

_____

CHAPTER 16
SALES: WARRANTIES

The seller in a sale of goods makes certain warranties. Chapter 16 is devoted to these warranties, and centers around two questions: What warranties does the seller make? How may the seller exclude or modify these warranties? You should observe (1) that the warranty of merchantability and the warranty of infringement apply only to merchants, (2) that the seller cannot disclaim the warranty protection given beneficiaries of the warranty, and (3) that the warranty of title and infringement are implied warranties but are not classified as either an express warranty or an implied warranty.

Fill-in Questions. *Write the correct word or words in the blank spaces to complete the following statements.*

1. The purpose of an implied warranty of _____ is to assure the buyer that he will have recourse against the seller if the title to the property proves deficient.
2. An implied warranty of fitness for a particular purpose is commonly referred to as a warranty of _____.
3. An implied warranty of merchantable quality is commonly referred to as a warranty of _____.
4. In the early history of the law of sales, the courts rigidly applied the maxim _____ "Let the buyer beware."
5. Implied warranties may arise from a course of dealing or _____.
6. No _____ with regard to defects arises when the buyer has examined the goods as fully as he desires or has _____ to examine the goods.
7. The maxim _____ means "Let the seller beware."
8. Statements which are the opinion or the belief only of the seller, commonly referred to as _____ or _____, are permissible in the law of sales.
9. A warranty made after a sale need not be supported by consideration since it is a _____.
10. A clause stating that the contract contains all the terms agreed upon is sometimes referred to as an _____.
11. There is a tendency on the part of the courts to abandon the _____ of contract rule.

12. _____ include words of commendation or praise, but _____ include words that are capable of proof or disproof.

True-False Questions. Indicate whether each of the following statements is true or false by circling the T or F.

T   *F*   1. An express warranty may be created in a sale by sample, model, or description.

T   *F*   2. A warranty of title is classified as an express warranty.

T   *F*   3. A warranty of infringement is classified as an implied warranty.

T   *F*   4. Warranty language will prevail over a disclaimer when the two cannot be reconciled.

T   *F*   5. A disclaimer of the warranty of merchantability must mention the word merchantability.

T   *F*   6. An implied warranty may not be excluded by a course of performance.

T   *F*   7. A purchaser of stolen property generally acquires no title.

T   *F*   8. A disclaimer of the warranty of fitness may be made either orally or in writing.

Problems. Analyze each of the following factual situations and state your decision and the reason for your decision in the space provided.

1. How may a sale by sample, model, or description be made?

_____

_____

_____

_____

_____

_____

_____

_____

_____

_____

_____

2. If a guest in the household of the buyer were made ill after eating tomatoes purchased from a grocer, would the guest have a right to recover from the grocer?

_____

_____

_____

_____

_____

_____

_____

_____

_____

_____

_____

_____

3. Plaintiff purchased at an auction an automobile for which he was unable to secure a certificate of title. He then brought an action against the auctioneer for breach of warranty. Decide.

_____

_____

_____

_____

_____

_____

_____

_____

_____

_____

_____

_____

_____

4. Mary, who wanted to purchase a ring with a blue stone, went to a jeweler to purchase the stone. A new salesman showed Mary a ring with a yellow and white stone and stated that he thought the ring was just as good as the ones with blue stones, that he believed it was worth $2,500, and that he would sell it to her for $1,000. Mary thereupon purchased the ring. Mary thereafter had the ring appraised, and the appraisal revealed that the ring was worth no more than $1,200. Would Mary prevail in an action against the jeweler for breach of warranty?

_____

_____

_____

_____

_____

_____

_____

_____

5. Brown purchased a new automobile from an automobile dealer, and the oral contract of sale provided: "It is expressly agreed that there are no warranties, express or implied, made by either the dealer or the manufacturer." Have the warranties of (1) merchantability, (2) fitness for a particular purpose, or (3) title been disclaimed?

_____

_____

_____

_____

_____

_____

_____

_____

_____

CHAPTER 17
SALES: PERFORMANCE

Chapter 17 states the rules governing the duties of the seller and the buyer in performing the sales contract. In addition to these duties, you will learn (1) when the risk of loss falls on the seller and when it falls on the buyer, (2) the excuses for nonperformance of the sales contract by the seller and by the buyer, (3) when the seller and the buyer have an insurable interest in the goods, (4) the right given the seller to "cure" when the buyer rejects nonconforming goods, (5) the right given the buyer to "cure" when the seller rejects a check in payment of the goods, and (6) the right of either the seller or the buyer to suspend performance.

Fill-in Questions. *Write the correct word or words in the blank spaces to complete the following statements.*

1. The seller performs when he tenders delivery of _____ goods to the buyer.
2. The tender of a _____ document of title or a written direction to the bailee to deliver is sufficient tender unless the buyer seasonably objects.
3. The tender of the goods may correctly be made by means of tendering documents of title through customary _____ channels.
4. The buyer has a right to accept only a part of the _____ units without incurring the risk of being liable for acceptance of all the units provided the goods fail to conform to the contract in any respect.
5. A _____ is a sale whereby the buyer contracts to pay for the goods when the draft with the documents attached is tendered for payment although the goods are still in transit.
6. The risk of loss passes to the buyer upon his receipt of the goods if the seller is a _____.
7. The seller is given the right to _____ when the buyer rejects nonconforming goods, and the buyer is given the right to _____ when the seller rejects a check in payment of the goods.
8. The buyer and the seller are both given a right to _____ of performance when either party is uncertain of performance by the other party.

True-False Questions. Indicate whether each of the following statements is true or false by circling the T or F.

T   F   1. The seller is given the right to "cure" when the buyer rejects nonconforming goods.

T   F   2. The seller's insurable interest always terminates when the goods are delivered to the buyer.

T   F   3. The buyer cannot have an insurable interest in the goods until the goods are in existence and identified as the subject matter of the contract.

T   F   4. Destruction of the subject matter of the contract will never excuse performance by the seller.

T   F   5. If the seller and the buyer do not agree on the time of delivery of the goods, the time is thirty days after payment is made.

T   F   6. The buyer is always justified in refusing to accept partial deliveries.

T   F   7. If no place or method of inspection is agreed upon, the buyer will be permitted to inspect the goods at the time and place of his receipt of the goods.

T   F   8. A c.o.d. contract for the shipment of goods gives the buyer the right to inspect the goods before payment.

T   F   9. In a shipment contract, the risk of loss passes to the buyer as soon as the buyer receives the goods.

T   F 10. In a destination contract, the risk of loss passes to the buyer when the seller has made a proper tender of delivery of conforming goods at the place of destination.

T   F 11. If the goods are held by a bailee, the risk of loss passes to the buyer when he receives a negotiable document of title covering the goods.

T   F 12. The risk of loss is on the seller if the buyer rejects the goods because they fail to conform to the contract.

T   F 13. If the buyer accepts the goods, he may not thereafter revoke the acceptance.

T   F 14. The notice of delivery of the goods must be given so as to enable the buyer to take possession of the goods at a reasonable hour.

Problems. Analyze each of the following factual situations and state your decision and the reason for your decision in the space provided.

1. The buyer ordered 50,000 cellophane bags from the seller for use in merchandising candies sold by the buyer in retail stores. The bags were to conform with the sample bag which the buyer submitted to the seller. The bags were delivered, and 10,000 were used. It was then learned for the first time that the bags were unsatisfactory. The buyer

thereupon paid for the 10,000 bags which were used and returned the remaining 40,000 bags. The seller contended that the use of 10,000 of the bags without complaint amounted to an acceptance of all of them. Is the contention of the seller correct?

_____

_____

_____

_____

_____

_____

2. In problem 1, would your answer be the same if the subject matter of the sales contract had been a truck and the engine was nonconforming?

_____

_____

_____

3. The buyer purchased a TV set from the seller. The seller delivered the TV set to the residence of the buyer, and the buyer offered a check in payment therefor. The seller demanded cash or a certified check. The TV set was delivered on Saturday, and the buyer was unable to produce the cash or a certified check until Monday because the banks were closed. The seller then refused to complete the sale. Was the seller justified in refusing to sell the TV set to the buyer?

_____

_____

_____

_____

4. The buyer and the seller entered into an agreement whereby the buyer agreed to purchase and the seller agreed to manufacture and deliver particular types and sizes of trailers. On March 1, 1965, the buyer transmitted a written order for two trailers to be delivered on May 1, 1965, but the manufacturing plant of the seller was completely de-

stroyed by fire on March 15, 1965. Should the buyer prevail in an action for breach of contract?

_____

_____

_____

_____

_____

_____

5. Brown, a manufacturer, and Jones, a dealer, entered into a written agreement whereby Brown agreed to sell refrigerators to Jones, and Jones agreed to pay for the refrigerators thirty days after delivery. Delivery was to be made in installments. Brown and Jones carried out the agreement for six months under strained relations, because deliveries were frequently two or three months late. Jones was forced to buy refrigerators elsewhere in order to supply refrigerators to his customers. Jones asked for assurances that future deliveries would be made on time, and Brown replied: "I will try." What remedy, if any, is available to Jones?

_____

_____

_____

_____

6. What are the rights and duties of the seller and the buyer (1) when the agreed method of transportation becomes impractical but when commercially reasonable substitute transportation is available, and (2) when the agreed manner of payment fails because of government regulation?

_____

_____

_____

_____

_____

_____

CHAPTER 18
SALES: REMEDIES

Chapter 18 begins by explaining when an acceptance of the goods by the buyer occurs. This chapter then explains in detail the (1) remedies of the seller prior to acceptance, (2) remedies of the seller after acceptance, (3) remedies of the buyer prior to acceptance, and (4) remedies of the buyer after acceptance.

Fill-in Questions. *Write the correct word or words in the blank spaces to complete the following statements.*

1. The seller may stop the goods in transit on grounds of _____ or on grounds of _____.
2. The right to stop the goods in transit for breach of contract or fraud is limited to delivery of _____ or _____ shipments.
3. The use of the words _____ or _____ or the like is not a discharge for any claim for damages for breach of contract.
4. The seller has the right for ten days after the buyer receives the goods to _____ the goods upon discovery of the buyer's insolvency.
5. A buyer who has not accepted the goods or who has justifiably revoked his acceptance is given a _____ remedy by purchasing the goods elsewhere.
6. The buyer loses his right of _____ after acceptance of the goods if the goods have undergone any substantial change in condition not caused by their own defects.
7. The meaning of the word _____ means that the buyer may deduct all or any part of the damages resulting from the breach from any part of the price still due under the same contract.
8. The rule which provides that the seller should not be required to perform if it is reasonably certain that the buyer cannot or will not perform exemplifies the rule which permits a party to _____ performance upon an _____ breach.

True-False Questions. *Indicate whether each of the following statements is true or false by circling the T or F.*

T   F   1.   The buyer is obligated to notify the seller of his right to recoup when the seller breaches the contract.

T   *F* 2. The measure of damages for breach of warranty is calculated at the time and place of acceptance of the goods.

T   *F* 3. The buyer loses his right to damages when he cancels the contract.

T   *F* 4. Cancellation of the contract by the seller terminates all unperformed obligations on the part of the seller but not on the part of the buyer.

T   *F* 5. A seller who has complied with the restrictions on resale is entitled to retain any profit made on any resale.

T   *F* 6. The buyer may recover damages for nonconformity of the goods in any manner which is reasonable.

T   *F* 7. An action for the purchase price is always available to the seller who is in possession of the goods.

T   *F* 8. A seller who has the right to resell the goods is required to sell identified goods, as well as futures, at public sale.

T   *F* 9. The seller is given the right to refuse to deliver goods on credit if the buyer is insolvent.

T   *F* 10. Acceptance of the goods is usually signified by the receipt and retention of the goods after an inspection reveals them to be conforming.

Problems. Analyze each of the following factual situations and state your decision and the reason for your decision in the space provided.

1. The seller, in Chicago, sold certain goods to the buyer, in San Francisco, which were to be paid for in ten days. In accordance with the agreement, the seller delivered the goods f.o.b. the carrier in Chicago. The seller then learned of the insolvency of the buyer. Does the seller have a right to stop the goods in transit?

_____

_____

_____

_____

2. In problem 1, suppose the First Bank had advanced the money to the buyer for the purpose of purchasing the goods. Would the First Bank have the right to stop the goods in transit?

_____

_____

_____

_____

3. A dealer purchased ten color TV sets from a wholesaler, and the sets were to be shipped by carrier. The wholesaler shipped the TV sets, and then learned that the dealer was insolvent. The wholesaler attempted to stop the TV sets in transit, but learned that they had been delivered to The Warehouse Company. The wholesaler then attempted to reclaim the TV sets, but five of them had been delivered to the dealer and had been sold in the ordinary course of business. What remedy, if any, is available to the wholesaler?

_____

_____

_____

_____

_____

_____

_____

_____

4. The buyer purchased a specific typewriter from the seller and paid a part of the purchase price. The typewriter was identified to the contract. The seller was declared insolvent the next day. The buyer tendered the balance of the purchase price and asked for delivery of the typewriter. The creditors of the seller contend they have a superior claim to the typewriter. Are the creditors correct?

_____

_____

_____

_____

_____

_____

_____

_____

5. Plaintiff ordered one crate of Grade A frozen cut corn from defendant. The corn was received and paid for, but about two weeks thereafter plaintiff discovered that the corn was Grade B. Six months later, plaintiff notified the defendant that the corn was nonconforming and that he was revoking his acceptance. Is plaintiff entitled to the return of the purchase price?

_____

_____

_____

_____

_____

_____

_____

_____

_____

_____

COMMERCIAL PAPER   4

**CHAPTER 19
NATURE OF
COMMERCIAL PAPER**

Chapter 19 constitutes an introduction to a type of written contract that may be used in lieu of money. You should learn to distinguish the various types of negotiable instruments before proceeding with the remaining chapters pertaining to commercial paper. You should certainly be familiar with the most important types of negotiable instruments—the promissory note, the draft, and the check—because reference will be made to these instruments through the remaining chapters in Part 4.

Fill-in Questions. *Write the correct word or words in the blank spaces to complete the following statements.*

1. A medium of exchange that can be used in lieu of money is known as a _____ instrument.
2. The origin of our present-day law of negotiable instruments was the

    _____.
3. A _____, briefly stated, contains a promise to pay a sum of money.
4. The person who is a party to a promissory note and who promises to pay is known as the _____.
5. The two kinds of _____ are the chattel mortgage note and the real estate mortgage note.
6. The two forms of bonds in common use are the _____ bonds and the _____ bonds.
7. The person to whom a promissory note is made payable is known as the _____.
8. A note which is secured by a pledge of shares of stock or other property is known as a _____ note.
9. The usual form of a _____ is drawn by the seller-drawer on the buyer-drawee, payable to the payee, usually the seller, at some future time, for the sale price of a shipment of goods.
10. The Code is applicable to both the _____ as well as the _____ letter of credit.

11. A _____ is a written acknowledgment by a bank of receipt of money with an engagement to repay the money.
12. A _____ draft is in the customary form of a personal check but is distinguishable because it is always drawn by one _____ upon another _____.
13. A _____ check is a particularly convenient and safe form in which to carry credit.
14. A _____ note is used to secure the purchase price of goods.
15. A _____, briefly stated, is an order from one person to another person to pay a third person a sum of money.
16. The person to whom a draft is addressed is known as the _____.

True-False Questions. Indicate whether each of the following statements is true or false by circling the T or F.

T   *F*   1. The Code classifies the letter of credit as a negotiable instrument.

T   *F*   2. The Code defines a check as a draft drawn on a bank and payable on demand.

T   *F*   3. A cashier's check is drawn by a bank on itself ordering itself to pay a stated sum of money.

T   *F*   4. A banker's acceptance is used under circumstances similar to those under which the trade acceptance is used.

T   *F*   5. A draft payable at a stated time in the future is known as a sight draft.

T   *F*   6. Judgment notes are used only in a limited number of states.

T   *F*   7. A draft payable at sight is known as a time draft.

T   *F*   8. A cashier's check is a check issued by the cashier of a bank and is commonly used for the same purpose as a traveler's check.

CHAPTER 20
FORM AND
INTERPRETATION

The essential elements of a negotiable instrument are stated and explained in Chapter 20. It is essential that these elements be memorized. An instrument that does not contain these elements is nonnegotiable, and you will later learn that there is an important distinction between negotiable and nonnegotiable instruments. If you do not learn the chapters on commercial paper chapter by chapter, you will be at a disadvantage as the study of these chapters progresses.

Fill-in Questions. *Write the correct word or words in the blank spaces to complete the following statements.*

1. A negotiable promissory note must contain a _____ to pay a sum certain in money.
2. A negotiable instrument must be payable on _____ or at a _____ time.
3. The words of negotiability are _____ and _____.
4. The sum to be paid in a negotiable instrument must be _____.
5. A clause which hastens the date of maturity of an instrument is called an _____ clause.
6. The promise or order in a negotiable instrument must be _____.
7. A _____ of judgment clause does not affect negotiability.
8. A negotiable draft must contain an _____.
9. The negotiability of an instrument is not affected by the fact that it is postdated, _____, or _____.
10. A _____ recital on an instrument does not affect negotiability.
11. A promise or order to pay out of a _____ fund is conditional.
12. The sum to be paid in a negotiable instrument must be payable in _____.

True-False Questions. *Indicate whether each of the following statements is true or false by circling the T or F.*

T   *F*   1. The payee must be named or otherwise indicated with reasonable certainty.

T	*F*	2.	A negotiable instrument may be in writing or it may be oral.
T	*F*	3.	The writing in a negotiable instrument, including the signature, may be in pencil.
T	*F*	4.	A draft must contain an unconditional promise to pay.
T	*F*	5.	The sum payable in a negotiable instrument is a sum certain, although it is to be paid by stated installments.
T	*F*	6.	A negotiable instrument must always be on a form supplied by a bank.
T	*F*	7.	A promissory note must contain an order upon a third person to pay.
T	*F*	8.	An instrument is payable on demand when no time of payment is specified in the instrument.
T	*F*	9.	Insecurity clauses in an instrument will destroy negotiability.
T	*F*	10.	A clause giving the maker the right to extend payment indefinitely is not payable at a definite time.
T	*F*	11.	An undated instrument payable "one month after date" is negotiable.
T	*F*	12.	An instrument is negotiable even though it is drawn payable to the order of the maker, the drawer, or the drawee.
T	*F*	13.	Instruments payable to the order of "Brown and Jones" may be negotiated by either Brown or Jones.
T	*F*	14.	Instruments payable to the order of an unincorporated association are not negotiable.
T	*F*	15.	An instrument will always be nonnegotiable unless the instrument states the consideration.
T	*F*	16.	A promise contained in an instrument to post additional collateral does not affect the negotiability of such instrument.
T	*F*	17.	An instrument will always be rendered nonnegotiable provided such instrument contains a "confession of judgment" clause.
T	*F*	18.	The negotiability of a promissory note is not affected by a clause in the instrument which is intended to waive the "homestead exemption" law with respect to the maker.
T	*F*	19.	A negotiable instrument must be under seal.
T	*F*	20.	An instrument must be treated as a draft in case the instrument is so ambiguous that it is barely possible to state definitely whether it is a note or a draft.
T	*F*	21.	In case of a discrepancy in the amount of a note or draft, the handwritten terms will control the typewritten terms.
T	*F*	22.	A provision for interest in an instrument means interest at the judgment rate unless the instrument provides differently.
T	*F*	23.	Two or more persons who sign as maker, acceptor, drawer,

or indorser as a part of the same transaction are jointly and severally liable unless the instrument provides differently.

T   *F*   24.   A signature on an instrument is treated as that of a maker unless the instrument clearly indicates the capacity in which the signature was made.

Problems. *Analyze each of the following factual situations and state your decision and the reason for your decision in the space provided.*

$150.00   Chicago, Illinois, *February 1*, 19 70
Four years - - - - - - - - - - - - - - - after date   *I*
promise to pay to the *order of Cash* - - - - - - - - - - - - -
One Hundred Fifty and No/100 - - - - - - - - - - Dollars
with interest at the rate of   6%   per annum, and after maturity at the legal rate, together with all taxes assessed upon said sum against the payee or holder of this note. This note is given in payment of one tractor.
(Signed)   *Jan Baker*

1. "With interest at the rate of 6 percent per annum, and after maturity at the legal rate." Does this provision make the sum of money of the above note uncertain?

_____

_____

_____

_____

2. Is the above note order or bearer paper?

_____

_____

_____

_____

_____

3. "This note is given in payment of one tractor." Does this provision prevent the above note from being negotiable?

_____

_____

_____

_____

_____

_____

_____

_____

_____

_____

$350.00	Miami, Florida, *February 1*, 19 70

Thirty days after delivery of one TV set pay to the order of *The Acme Television Company* - - - - - - - - - -
Three Hundred and 50/100 - - - - - - - - - - - - - Dollars

To: *Ben Roberts or*
      Tom Brown   (Signed)   *Gary Gerson*
      Miami, Florida

---

4. Is the preceding draft addressed to a drawee with reasonable certainty?

_____

_____

_____

_____

_____

_____

_____

_____

_____

5. State the changes that would make the preceding draft negotiable.

_____
_____
_____
_____
_____
_____
_____
_____
_____

6. What is the amount of the preceding draft?

_____
_____
_____
_____
_____
_____

$2,000.00   Houston, Texas, January 1, 1970
At the dates hereinafter mentioned, for value received,
I promise to pay to Ben Price the sum of Two
Thousand Dollars, payable in installments as follows:
Five Hundred Dollars on the first day of January,
1971, and Five Hundred Dollars on the first day of
January of each and every year thereafter until and
including the first day of January, 1974, with interest
at the rate of 6 percent per annum after maturity;
and it is further agreed that on default in the payment
of any installment the whole amount of this note
shall then become due and payable at the election
of the holder hereof.

(Signed)   *Jan Baker*

---

7. "... and it is further agreed that on default in the payment of any installment the whole amount of this note shall then become due and

payable at the election of the holder hereof." Does this make the time of payment of the above installment note uncertain?

_____

_____

_____

_____

8. Is the preceding installment note negotiable?

_____

_____

_____

_____

9. An instrument was made payable to the "order of the Jones Foundation Fund." Explain whether this quoted provision does or does not destroy negotiability.

_____

_____

_____

_____

_____

10. State in the space provided whether the use of the following words makes the instrument order paper or bearer paper.
    (a) Pay to the order of cash.   _____
    (b) Pay Smith or bearer.   _____
    (c) Pay to the order of _____.   _____
    (d) The printed form of the in-   _____
    strument is in this style: "Pay to
    the order of _____ or bearer,"
    and the instrument is filled in with
    the name of the payee.
    (e) The printed form of the in-   _____
    strument is in this style: "Pay to
    the order of _____," and the in-
    strument is filled in with the name
    of the payee, coupled with the
    words "or bearer."

CHAPTER 21
TRANSFER AND
NEGOTIATION

Chapter 21 defines negotiation, explains how an instrument should be negotiated, and distinguishes between the transfer of an instrument and the negotiation of an instrument. This chapter is neither long nor difficult. It is important, however, that you learn the effect of the different kinds of indorsements and how an instrument should be delivered to the transferee.

Fill-in Questions. *Write the correct word or words in the blank spaces to complete the following statements.*

1. _____ is the transfer of an instrument in such form that the transferee becomes a holder.

2. An indorsement, unless it is made by the use of an _____, must be written on the instrument itself.

3. The signature of the indorser, without anything more, written upon the back of an instrument is a _____ indorsement.

4. A _____ indorsement restricts the right of the indorsee in some way.

5. A _____ indorsement specifies the person to whom, or to whose order, the instrument is to be payable.

6. The person to whom an order instrument is transferred without an indorsement is a _____.

7. The person who indorses an instrument is known as an _____.

8. The person to whom an instrument is negotiated by indorsement and delivery is an _____.

9. The indorser may disclaim his liability on the instrument by indorsing the instrument with the words _____.

True-False Questions. *Indicate whether each of the following statements is true or false by circling the T or F.*

T   F   1. Words of assignment added to an indorsement prohibit the further negotiation of the instrument.

T   F   2. The duty to act consistently with an indorsement to a fiduciary is limited to the first taker.

T   F   3. Indorsements "for collection" are qualified indorsements.

T	*F*	4.	Indorsements such as "Pay Davis only" prohibit the further negotiation of the instrument.
T	*F*	5.	The last indorsement on an instrument controls the further negotiation of the instrument.
T	*F*	6.	A payee whose name is misspelled may effectively negotiate the instrument by indorsing the instrument using the misspelled name.
T	*F*	7.	An indorsement is customarily and properly written on the back of the instrument.
T	*F*	8.	A mere surrender of an instrument to a drawee-bank is a transfer by assignment.

Problems. Analyze each of the following factual situations and state your decision and the reason for your decision in the space provided.

1. The maker made a note payable to the order of the payee. The payee transferred by delivery this note for value and before maturity to Boles. Was this a proper negotiation by the payee to Boles?

_____

_____

_____

_____

_____

_____

2. The manager of a store should indorse checks received in payment of goods sold in such a manner that a dishonest employee, thief, or robber could not obtain the proceeds of such checks. What indorsement should be used? Give an example.

_____

_____

_____

_____

_____

_____

84

3. Plaintiff, an infant, purchased an automobile from defendant. Plaintiff gave defendant a check for $1,400 in payment of the car. Defendant then purchased an automobile from a dealer, and indorsed and delivered the $1,400 check given him by plaintiff in partial payment of the automobile. Plaintiff thereafter brought an action against the dealer alleging that he had disaffirmed the purchase of the automobile, and sought to recover the $1,400 check. Should plaintiff recover?

4. The maker made a note payable to the payee or bearer. The payee indorsed it specially to Adams. Adams delivered it to a holder without indorsing it. Is the holder a bearer in possession of bearer paper?

5. Smith, the payee of a note which was secured by a mortgage, sold the the note to Jones, placed his indorsement on the mortgage, and delivered the note and mortgage to Jones. Is this a proper negotiation?

_____

_____

_____

_____

_____

_____

_____

_____

_____

_____

_____

CHAPTER 22
HOLDERS IN
DUE COURSE

A holder in due course must first be a holder before he can qualify as a holder in due course, and the last chapter explained the requirements for a person to become a holder. Chapter 22 explains the conditions under which a holder must take the instrument in order to qualify as a holder in due course. It is important that you thoroughly understand these conditions before proceeding with the next chapter; otherwise the next chapter will be difficult to understand. It is also important to understand (1) that a holder may comply with these conditions but not qualify as a holder in due course if his successor in interest was not a holder in due course, and (2) that a reacquirer may be a holder in due course even though he takes the instrument from a person who was not a holder in due course.

Fill-in Questions. Write the correct word or words in the blank spaces to complete the following statements.

1. A holder gives value to the extent that he acquires a _____ in or a lien on the instrument.

2. A holder gives value when he makes an _____ commitment to a third person.

3. A holder in due course is a holder who takes the instrument for _____, without notice that it is _____, without notice that it has been _____, without notice of any _____ against or _____ to it on the part of any person, and in _____.

4. A purchaser cannot qualify as a holder in due course if he has reason to know that a _____ for payment of the instrument was made and such payment was refused.

5. A purchaser who takes an instrument without notice that it has been presented and _____ may take the instrument as a holder in due course.

6. _____ permeates all the requirements that are essential for a person to qualify as a holder in due course.

7. A purchaser has notice of a claim against the instrument when he has

knowledge that a _____ has negotiated the instrument in payment of, or as security for, his own debt or benefit.

8. A _____ is remitted to his former position.

True-False Questions. Indicate whether each of the following statements is true or false by circling the T or F.

T *F* 1. The meanings of "value" and "consideration" are identical.

T *F* 2. A negotiable instrument may not be transferred if it is overdue or has been dishonored.

T *F* 3. A purchaser would be a holder in due course if he had no reason to know that past-due installments have not been paid.

T *F* 4. A holder gives value when he gives a negotiable instrument in exchange for a negotiable instrument.

T *F* 5. An instrument with a fixed maturity designated by a calendar date is overdue at the beginning of the day after the fixed date.

T *F* 6. A purchaser of an incomplete order instrument which has been completed is a holder in due course unless he has notice that the completion was improper.

T *F* 7. A purchaser who takes an instrument with notice that an indorser has been discharged is not a holder in due course.

T *F* 8. A person is not required to search the public records for possible defenses before purchasing a negotiable instrument.

T *F* 9. A holder becomes a holder in due course if he merely takes the instrument as a successor in interest to a prior holder who was not himself a holder in due course.

T *F* 10. Any apparent alterations, erasures, or discrepancies in the name of the payee, the amount, the due date, or the interest constitute a material alteration.

Problems. Analyze each of the following factual situations and state your decision and the reason for your decision in the space provided.

$ _____   _____ 19___

_____ Pay to

the order of _____

_____ Dollars

Value rec'd and charge to account of

To_____

_____ } _____

1. Bob Clark, of 1234 Main Street, Los Angeles, California, owes Jack Kelley, of Boston, Massachusetts, the sum of $250, which will mature on July 1, 1970. Jack Kelley owes Tom Bryan, of Los Angeles, California, the sum of $250, which will also mature on July 1, 1970. Assuming you are the duly authorized agent of Jack Kelley, fill in the blank spaces in the preceding form so that the completed form may be mailed to Tom Bryan, who will present it to Bob Clark for payment.

$240.50   Washington, D. C., *July 1*, 19 *70* No. *118*

Four years - - - - - - - - - - - - - after date, the
undersigned promises to pay to the order of
The Acme Electric Company - - - - - - - - - - - - - - - - -
Two Hundred Forty and 50/100 - - - - - - - - - *Dollars*
with interest at   *6%*   per annum payable
semiannually on January 1 and July 1. If interest is not
paid when due, both principal and accrued interest
shall bear interest at the rate of   *8%*   per annum.
On default of any of the installments of interest, the
principal shall then become due and payable at the
option of the holder. The holder may also accelerate
the maturity of the principal whenever he deems
himself insecure. This note is given in payment of one
TV set and is subject to a mortgage on same of
even date.

                              (Signed)   *Jan Baker*

---

2. James purchased the preceding note with knowledge that the last installment of interest was overdue. Would this alone prevent James from being a holder in due course?

_____

_____

_____

_____

_____

_____

3. Brown purchased the preceding note with knowledge that The Acme Electric Company had refused to deliver the TV set to Baker. Would this alone prevent Brown from being a holder in due course?

4. Baker defaulted in an installment of interest, and the holder exercised his right to accelerate the maturity date of the preceding note. If Black purchased the note one week after the acceleration and without knowledge that the prior holder had accelerated the maturity date of the note, would the prior acceleration alone prevent him from being a holder in due course?

5. Could a purchaser of the preceding note who bought for value, without notice that it was overdue or had been dishonored or of any defense against or claim to it on the part of any person, and in good faith qualify as a holder in due course?

_____

_____

_____

_____

_____

_____

_____

_____

$500.00   Dallas, Texas, *January 1*, 19 ___

In ten equal payments as herein provided, for value received, - - - - - - - - - - *the undersigned* - - - - - - - - - - promises to pay to *Tom Smith* - - - - - - - - - - the sum of *Five Hundred and No/100* - - - - - - - - - - - - - Dollars.

The maker agrees to pay the above obligation in ten installments of fifty dollars ($50) each, beginning on the first day of January of the date hereon, and continuing such payments on the first day of each and every month thereafter until the entire indebtedness shall have been paid in full. On default of any of the above installments, the whole amount remaining unpaid shall then become due and payable at the option of the holder.

(Signed)   *Bob Taylor*

---

6. On January 1, 1970, Smith sold a radio to Taylor for $500, at which time Taylor made and delivered to Smith the preceding note. It was agreed that Smith would deliver the radio to Taylor's house on January 2, 1970. On January 3, 1970, Smith indorsed the preceding note in blank and delivered it to his son John as a birthday gift. Smith failed to deliver the radio in accordance with their agreement, and Taylor has refused to pay any part of the note. John elected to declare all

the installments due and brought an action against Taylor to collect on the above note. Taylor alleges a total failure of consideration as a defense. Decide.

_____

_____

_____

_____

_____

_____

_____

_____

_____

_____

CHAPTER 23
DEFENSES

Chapter 23 explains the defenses which may be offered by the defendant in an action as a reason why the plaintiff should not recover what he seeks. The distinction between a holder and a holder in due course must be kept clearly in mind, because personal defenses may be used against a holder but not a holder in due course. The real defenses, however, may be used against any holder, including a holder in due course. You should observe that some of the defenses which are classified as real defenses are also sometimes classified as personal defenses. It is a matter of analyzing the facts of the particular case.

Fill-in Questions. *Write the correct word or words in the blank spaces to complete the following statements.*

1. Defenses are classified as _____ and _____ defenses.
2. _____ defenses may be used to defeat any action brought by any holder, including a holder in due course.
3. The defense of fraud in the execution may be asserted against a holder in due course if the maker is _____ ignorant.
4. The distinction between personal and real defenses becomes unimportant as between the _____ parties.
5. A holder in due course and a holder through a holder in due course take the instrument free of _____ defenses.
6. A _____ is that which may be offered by the defendant in an action as a reason why the plaintiff should not recover what he seeks.
7. Fraud in the _____ is a personal defense.
8. Fraud in the _____ is a real defense.
9. An alteration is a _____ alteration when it changes the contract of a party to an instrument.
10. A party whose signature was forged or used without _____ has a real defense against a holder in due course.
11. The defense of material alteration is not available to any person who by his _____ substantially contributes to the material alteration.

12. Duress is only a _____ defense when the force and pressure used consists only of threats.

True-False Questions. Indicate whether each of the following statements is true or false by circling the T or F.

T   *F*   1.   Nondelivery of a completed instrument is a real defense.
T   *F*   2.   Delivery of an incomplete instrument is a personal defense.
T   *F*   3.   Payment of an instrument prior to maturity is a personal defense.
T   *F*   4.   Conditional delivery of a completed instrument is a personal defense.
T   *F*   5.   Nondelivery of an incomplete instrument is a personal defense.
T   *F*   6.   Payment of an instrument to the wrong person is a real defense.
T   *F*   7.   Discharge of all indorsers is a real defense.
T   *F*   8.   Incapacity of a party is always a real defense.
T   *F*   9.   A material alteration is a real defense to the extent of the alteration.
T   *F*   10. Illegality is always a real defense.
T   *F*   11. A person who signs an instrument under direct compulsion which seriously threatens him with actual physical harm may assert a real defense against a holder in due course.
T   *F*   12. A discharge in bankruptcy is a real defense.

Problems. Analyze each of the following factual situations and state your decision and the reason for your decision in the space provided.

1.   The drawer drew a check to the order of the payee, but the amount was left blank. The drawer, not knowing the amount he owed the payee, mailed the check to the payee with instructions to fill it in for the correct amount. The amount owed was $125. The payee, without authority, sold the check for $1,000 to Jones, who did not know that the payee wrongfully completed the check for $1,000. The drawer stopped payment on the check. The check was not paid by the drawee-bank, and Jones brought an action against the drawer on the check. What defense, if any, does the drawer have?

_____

_____

_____

_____

_____

2. Same facts as problem 1 except that the payee, after he filled in the check for $1,000, brought an action against the drawer on the check. What defense, if any, does the drawer have?

_____

_____

_____

_____

_____

_____

_____

_____

3. The maker made a completed promissory note payable to the order of cash and left it on his desk. A thief stole the note and negotiated it to Jones, a holder in due course. Does the maker have an effective defense against Jones?

_____

_____

_____

_____

4. Same facts as problem 3 except that the name of the payee was left blank; the amount of the note was left blank; the maker locked the note in a safe; and a thief removed the note from the safe, filled it in for $5,000, and made himself the payee. If this note is transferred before maturity to Jones, an innocent purchaser for value, will Jones be able to collect from the maker?

_____

_____

_____

_____

```
$100.00                New York, New York, July 1, 1970
One year after date, I promise to pay to the order of
Kay Brown, One Hundred and No/100 dollars. This
note is given in payment of a used record player.
                    (Signed)    Mary Smith
```

5. The preceding note was made by Smith and delivered to Brown in payment for a used record player which Brown fraudulently stated had been reconditioned with new parts. The record player had not been so reconditioned, and it ceased to operate two days after the sale. On July 2, 1970, Brown sold the preceding note for $90 to Sims, who bought in good faith and without any knowledge of Brown's fraud. If Smith refuses to pay Sims on the date of maturity, how much, if any, can Sims recover by suing Smith?

_____

_____

_____

_____

_____

_____

_____

_____

6. If the note had read, ". . . I promise to pay Kay Brown. . . ," would your answer be the same?

_____

_____

_____

_____

_____

_____

_____

_____

CHAPTER 24
PRESENTMENT,
NOTICE OF DISHONOR,
PROTEST

*The conditions precedent to enforcing the liability of
drawers of checks and drafts and all unqualified indorsers are explained in Chapter 24. You should learn
(1) the drafts that must be presented for acceptance,
(2) how checks and drafts are accepted by the drawee,
(3) the rights and duties of the parties in making presentment for payment, (4) the steps that are required
to be taken in giving notice of dishonor to the parties
secondarily liable, and (5) when the presentment,
notice of dishonor, and protest are delayed or excused.*

*Fill-in Questions. Write the correct word or words in the blank spaces to
complete the following statements.*

1. The Code uses the words _____ and entirely
   _____ with respect to presentment, notice of
   dishonor, and protest.
2. An instrument made payable at a bank is known as a _____
   instrument.
3. A _____ is a written notice that an instrument
   has been presented for acceptance or payment, as the case may be,
   and that it has been dishonored.
4. One of the objects of giving _____ is to in-
   form the parties secondarily liable that the maker or acceptor, as the
   case may be, has failed to meet his obligation.
5. The most usual mode of acceptance is the writing of the word "accepted" across the _____ of the draft, fol-
   lowed by the date and the signature of the drawee.
6. Presentment, notice of dishonor, and sometimes protest are important
   _____ to enforcing the liability of drawers of
   checks and drafts and all unqualified indorsers.
7. The purpose of the _____ rule is to allow a
   bank additional time to examine carefully the accompanying documents before making payment.
8. The view of the _____ and _____
   with respect to presentment of bank-domiciled instruments is that an
   instrument so payable is only a designation of the place of payment.

True-False Questions. Indicate whether each of the following statements is true or false by circling the T or F.

T F 1. The drawing of a draft and its delivery to the payee obligates the drawee to pay the draft.

T F 2. A draft is dishonored unless the drawee accepts it immediately.

T F 3. Each drawer and indorser who does not affirmatively assent to the acceptance varying the draft is discharged.

T F 4. Promissory notes and accepted drafts must be presented for payment in order to charge the person secondarily liable in case the instrument is not paid.

T F 5. The risk of the bank's insolvency after the maturity of a bank-domiciled instrument is placed on the maker or acceptor.

T F 6. A draft payable at sight is payable on presentment and need not be presented for acceptance.

T F 7. Instruments payable at a stated date must be presented for payment on the stated date.

T F 8. Presentment for acceptance or payment must be made to all the persons where there are two or more persons to whom presentment may be made.

T F 9. Instruments payable at a stated date, or at a fixed period after a stated date, must be presented for acceptance on or before the date on which the instrument is payable.

T F 10. Delay is not excused even though the party has acted with reasonable diligence and the delay is not his fault.

Problems. Analyze each of the following factual situations and state your decision and the reason for your decision in the space provided.

1. Brown indorsed a note in blank to Cabot which contained the following: "The makers, indorsers, sureties, guarantor, and assigns of this note severally waive demand, presentment for payment, protest, notice of protest and of nonpyament." Cabot forgot to present the note to the maker for payment until three months after the date of maturity. The maker was insolvent and, therefore, unable to pay the note. Three weeks later, Cabot met Brown on the street and demanded payment of the note. Is Brown correct when he argues that he has been discharged of his secondary liability as an indorser?

_____

_____

_____

_____

_____

_____

_____

2. Baker executed a $1,000 negotiable promissory note to Cabot. Cabot indorsed this note to Drake, who presented the note for payment three days after the date of maturity. What are the rights of Drake with respect to recovering from Baker or Cabot?

_____

_____

_____

_____

_____

_____

_____

3. Davis executed a promissory note for $1,000, payable to the order of plaintiff, and the note was indorsed by defendant. The note was presented for payment, payment was refused, and the note was protested. A notice of dishonor was sent by registered mail to defendant at his residence, and the letter was returned by the post office. The notation "refused" was written across the face of the letter. Defendant contended that there must be an actual receipt of the notice when registered mail is used to give notice of dishonor. Do you agree with this contention?

_____

_____

_____

_____

_____

_____

4. The holder of a note demanded payment of the note from the maker, and the maker of the note demanded the holder to produce the note. The holder could not produce the note because it was in his safe-deposit box. The holder thereafter sent a notice of dishonor to the indorser and advised him that he would be required to pay the note. What remedy, if any, is available to the indorser?

_____

_____

_____

_____

_____

_____

_____

_____

_____

5. What are the three situations when presentment of a draft for acceptance, unless excused, is a required proceeding before an action may be brought against the drawer or an indorser?

_____

_____

_____

_____

_____

_____

_____

_____

_____

CHAPTER 25
LIABILITY OF PARTIES

The purpose of Chapter 25 is to explain who the primary and secondary parties are and to discuss their liability. You should learn these liabilities and the liability of accommodation parties, a guarantor, an authorized and unauthorized agent, and corporate officers. Particular attention should be given to the three situations in which an indorsement by any person in the name of a named payee is effective to transfer the instrument. The warranties are technical, but you must learn these warranties if you are to understand the liabilities of the parties.

Fill-in Questions. *Write the correct word or words in the blank spaces to complete the following statements.*

1. All parties to an instrument incur a _____ liability unless they disclaim their liability.
2. An acceptor is _____ liable to the holder for payment of an instrument.
3. The Code recognizes that an accommodation party is a _____.
4. A person presenting an instrument for payment makes certain warranties to the _____ or _____.
5. The parties having a secondary liability are the _____ and _____.
6. The warranty of title permits the _____ or _____ to recover from the person presenting the instrument when an indorsement turns out to be forged.
7. The warranties on transfer run against the _____.
8. A transferor indorsing _____ warrants only that he has no knowledge of any defense of any party that is good against him.
9. By putting an instrument in circulation the maker and acceptor admit that the _____ exists and has the capacity to _____ the instrument.
10. If an accommodation party pays the instrument, he has a right of recourse against the _____ party.
11. In impersonation cases, the loss falls upon the maker or drawer irrespective of whether the impersonation is _____ imposture or imposture by _____.

True-False Questions. Indicate whether each of the following statements is true or false by circling the T or F.

T F 1. The drawer cannot escape payment of a check or draft by showing the nonexistence or incapacity of the payee.

T F 2. The liability of an indorser runs only to subsequent indorsers.

T F 3. An accommodation party is one who signs the instrument in any capacity for the purpose of lending his name to another party to the instrument.

T F 4. An irregular indorsement is notice to all persons of the accommodation character of the instrument.

T F 5. A guaranty of collection requires that the holder first proceed against the maker or acceptor.

T F 6. An individual who is the sole proprietor of a business which he operates under a trade name may not sign an instrument in the trade name.

T F 7. In padded payroll cases, the loss falls upon the employer rather than upon a subsequent holder.

T F 8. The warranty against material alteration permits the payor who pays a materially altered check to recover from the drawer.

T F 9. The warranties on transfer run to the transferee only when the transfer is made by delivery.

T F 10. The warranty of good title on transfer permits the transferee to recover from the transferor when an indorsement is forged.

Problems. Analyze each of the following factual situations and state your decision and the reason for your decision in the space provided.

1. The maker made a note payable to the order of the payee, who indorsed it in blank and delivered it to Ben Adams. Adams indorsed the note, "Pay James Brown, without recourse, Ben Adams." Brown presented the note to the maker for payment at the date of maturity, but the maker dishonored it because of insolvency. Does Brown have a right to recover from Adams?

_____

_____

_____

_____

_____

_____

_____

_____

_____

_____

_____

2. Adams forged the name of B. B. Brown as the maker on a promissory note and named J. J. Jones as the payee. Jones presented the note to Brown when the note became due, and Brown stated that his signature had been forged. Brown, therefore, refused to pay the note. Jones then brought an action against Adams to collect the amount of the note. The defense of Adams was the well-recognized rule that "no person is liable on an instrument unless his signature appears thereon." Is this defense available to Adams?

_____

_____

_____

_____

_____

_____

_____

_____

_____

_____

3. The maker made a note payable to the order of the payee for $25, but blank spaces were negligently left before the number "25" as well as the word "twenty-five." The payee, without authority, inserted the number "5" in front of the number "25" and "five hundred" in front of the word "twenty-five," thereby raising the amount of the note to $525. The payee then transferred the note to Adams, an innocent purchaser, for value and before maturity. Adams transferred the note to Brown by indorsing, "Pay James Brown, without recourse, Ben Adams." Brown presented the note to the maker for payment, and the

maker paid him $25. Does Brown have a right to recover $475 from Adams?

_____

_____

_____

_____

_____

_____

_____

_____

_____

_____

4. Jim Jones, the agent of Mary Jones, who was not identified in the note, signed a promissory note for $500 in the following form: "Jim Jones, Agent." Smith, who was the payee, negotiated the note to Brown, who took the note as a holder in due course. Is Jim Jones personally obligated on the note?

_____

_____

_____

_____

_____

_____

_____

_____

_____

_____

5. The payee, Williams, drew a draft for $600 and forged the name of the drawer. The payee then transferred the draft to Adams by indorsing in blank and delivering it to Adams. Adams transferred the draft to Brown, who presented it to the drawee for acceptance. The drawee, realizing that he owed the drawer $500, wrote the date, the word "accepted," and signed his name across the face of the draft. Brown transferred the accepted draft to Cabot, an innocent purchaser, before maturity and for value. The drawee-acceptor learned prior to the date of maturity that the signature of the drawer was forged. Does the forged signature of the drawer excuse the acceptor from paying the draft in these circumstances?

_____

_____

_____

_____

_____

_____

_____

_____

_____

_____

_____

_____

_____

_____

_____

_____

_____

_____

6. Brown, the treasurer of the X Corporation, drew a corporate check and named Mary, his secretary, as the payee. Brown did not, however, intend that Mary should receive the check. The signature of the corporation was made by the use of a rubber stamp, which was the usual method of signing. Brown then indorsed the name of Mary,

cashed the check, and absconded. Should the bank or the corporation stand the loss?

_____

_____

_____

_____

_____

_____

_____

_____

_____

_____

_____

CHAPTER 26
DISCHARGE

Chapter 26 explains how a party is discharged from his liability on the instrument. This chapter is neither long nor technical, as were some of the other chapters in Part 4, "Commercial Paper." You will do well, however, to remember that an accommodation party is a surety. The principles of suretyship law discussed in this chapter, therefore, should be applied to the liability of accommodation parties discussed in the last chapter.

Fill-in Questions. *Write the correct word or words in the blank spaces to complete the following statements.*

1. Payment will not result in the discharge of the liability of a person who makes payment in a manner inconsistent with the terms of a _____ indorsement.

2. The Code provides that intervening parties are discharged where a holder _____ the instrument.

3. The Code provides that an alteration by a holder which is both _____ and _____ discharges any party when the contract of such party is changed.

4. No discharge of any party is effective against a _____ unless he has notice of such discharge when he takes the instrument.

5. _____ must be done in any manner apparent on the face of the instrument.

6. _____ may be accomplished by a signed writing delivered to the party to be discharged.

True-False Questions. *Indicate whether each of the following statements is true or false by circling the T or F.*

T *F* 1. An adverse claimant may restrain payment of an instrument by supplying an adequate indemnity.

T *F* 2. Payment of an instrument does not result in discharge of liability of a person who in bad faith pays a holder who acquired the instrument by theft.

T *F* 3. The maker or acceptor must be able and ready to pay an instrument at each place when the instrument is payable at any one of two or more specified places.

T   *F*   4. The express purpose of reacquiring an instrument is normally for the purpose of discharging the maker from liability.

T   *F*   5. A novation will discharge all parties who are liable on an instrument.

Problems. Analyze each of the following factual situations and state your decision and the reason for your decision in the space provided.

1. The holder of a draft on which appeared the defendant's acceptance accidentally tore it in two pieces. He then pasted the two pieces together and sold it to plaintiff. The defendant-acceptor refused to pay the draft when it was presented for payment. Is the defendant-acceptor correct when he argues that the draft was discharged by cancellation?

---

2. Brown was the holder of a promissory note for $300, which was signed by Smith as the maker. Brown negotiated the note to Jones, who negotiated the note to Davis. Davis purchased certain merchandise from Brown and gave this same note to Brown in payment of the merchandise. Brown immediately called Jones by telephone and stated that he was canceling the liability of Jones as an indorser on the note. Brown did not, however, make any notation on the note. Two days later, Brown negotiated the note to Orr, a holder in due course. Smith, the maker, was unable to pay the note on its date of maturity. Orr then attempted to recover the $300 from Jones. Is Jones liable?

---

3. Baker was the holder of a $100 note, which was signed by Abel as the maker, and payable on July 1, 1970. Baker and Abel met on June 30, 1970, at which time Abel offered Baker twenty-five boxes of citrus in settlement of the note. Baker agreed, and the citrus was delivered to and accepted by Baker. Baker promised Abel to cancel the note and deliver it to Abel the next day. Baker did not cancel the note, but he did sell it to Jay, a holder in due course, in the afternoon of June 30, 1970. Jay presented the note to Abel for payment the next day. Abel refused to pay the note, and Jay brought an action against Abel to recover the $100. Is Abel liable?

_____

_____

_____

_____

_____

_____

_____

4. Black was the holder in due course of a note signed by Smith, as maker, in the amount of $500. Black was heavily indebted to White, who claimed that Smith should pay him the $500, and White threatened to sue Smith if Smith did not pay. On the date of maturity of the note, Black was paid the $500 when he presented the note to Smith for payment. White claims that the note was not discharged and that he has a right to recover the $500 from Smith. Is this contention correct?

_____

_____

_____

_____

_____

_____

_____

5. Cobb was a holder in due course of a note in the amount of $5,000. The note was negotiated to the following persons who became holders in due course: Cobb to Webb; Webb to Stone; and Stone to Breck. Breck then negotiated the note to Cobb in payment of an antecedent debt. Cobb reacquired the note the day before maturity of the note. He did make a proper presentment of the note to the maker on the following day, and the note was dishonored. Does Cobb have a right to recover the amount of the note from Webb, a wealthy merchant?

_____

_____

_____

_____

_____

_____

_____

_____

_____

**CHAPTER 27
RELATIONSHIP
BETWEEN PAYOR BANK
AND ITS CUSTOMER**

The purpose of Chapter 27 is to discuss some of the rights and duties of the bank and the customer. The principles of law are simple, but this does not mean that the principles are not important. You should particularly observe (1) that a certification of a check is an acceptance of the check and that the customer has no right to stop payment on a certified check, (2) the method of stopping payment on a check, and (3) the duty of the customer to promptly examine his bank statement and canceled checks.

Fill-in Questions. *Write the correct word or words in the blank spaces to complete the following statements.*

1. A deposit in a bank is either a _____ or a _____ deposit.

2. A check which is presented to the bank on which it is drawn is known as an _____ check.

3. _____ of a check is an acceptance of the check.

4. A bank is given the right of _____ if the bank improperly pays a check over a stop order.

5. A general deposit creates a debtor-creditor relationship, and the depositor is the _____ and the bank is the _____.

6. The customer is limited by the _____ for a period of one year in which to report any forgeries of his signature and alterations of checks.

7. A _____ check is one that is presented for payment an unusually long time after the date of the check.

True-False Questions. *Indicate whether each of the following statements is true or false by circling the T or F.*

T   F   1. The customer is limited by the statute of limitations for a period of three years in which to report forged indorsements.

T   *F*   2. A bank that pays a check with a forged signature cannot debit the account of the drawer for any amount.

T   *F*   3. A deposit will be deemed a special deposit unless the customer and the bank agree that it is to be a general deposit.

T   *F*   4. A depositor has the right to draw checks on a savings account.

T   *F*   5. The Code provides that a member of a joint account may not stop payment of a check when the check is drawn by another member.

T   *F*   6. The drawer cannot stop payment on a certified check.

T   *F*   7. A refusal to pay an apparently stale check is a wrongful dishonor if the bank later learns that the check is not stale.

T   *F*   8. A bank is not permitted to provide missing indorsements on checks.

T   *F*   9. A bank cannot by agreement disclaim its responsibility for its own lack of good faith or failure to exercise ordinary care.

Problems. *Analyze each of the following factual situations and state your decision and the reason for your decision in the space provided.*

1. Davis gave Daniel a check for $500, and Daniel negotiated the check to Aaron by indorsement and delivery. Aaron deposited the check in his bank the next day, but the check was returned by the drawee-bank marked "insufficient funds." Davis died two months thereafter, and Aaron filed a claim against the estate of Davis to recover the $500. The executor of the estate of Davis contended that the check was a nullity because Araon had failed to deposit the check within a reasonable time. Do you agree with this contention?

_____

_____

_____

_____

_____

_____

_____

_____

_____

_____

2. On December 1, 1970, Brown gave Jones a check for $100, and Jones presented the check to the drawee-bank for payment the next morning. A teller at the drawee-bank told Jones to return before the bank closed for the day, at which time the check would be paid. Jones demanded immediate payment. Is the drawee-bank under a duty to pay or dishonor the check immediately?

_____

_____

_____

_____

_____

_____

_____

_____

_____

_____

3. Barsh, the day before he was killed in an automobile accident, had given the X Company a check in payment of certain merchandise. The X Company presented the check for payment the next day, and the drawee-bank paid the check. The executor of the estate of Barsh contended that the drawee-bank was under a duty to refuse payment because of the death of Barsh. Do you agree with this contention?

_____

_____

_____

_____

_____

_____

_____

4. Explain why a written order to stop payment on checks is preferable to oral orders to stop payment.

_____

_____

_____

_____

_____

_____

_____

_____

_____

BAILMENTS; DOCUMENTS OF TITLE

5

CHAPTER 28
BAILMENTS

Chapter 28 is devoted to bailments other than those governed by Article 7, "Documents of Title." You should understand the following before proceeding with the next chapter: (1) the distinction between bailments and similar transactions as well as the distinction between the types of bailments, (2) the degree of care that should be exercised by the bailee, (3) the rights and duties of the bailor and the bailee, (4) the rules of law found in the special bailment situations, (5) the termination of a bailment, and (6) the liens on personal property, particularly the artisan's lien.

Fill-in Questions. *Write the correct word or words in the blank spaces to complete the following statements.*

1. A bailment for the sole benefit of the _____ results when one person renders some service for another person without compensation in respect to the bailed property.

2. Property which has been lawfully taken by authority of legal process and is in the possession of a public officer is an illustration of _____ as distinguished from a bailment.

3. The essence of a bailment is that one person, called the _____, gives the possession and control of personal property to another person, called the _____.

4. A bailment for the sole benefit of the _____ exists when one person borrows some item of personal property from another person.

5. The most common type of bailment is a bailment for the _____ of the parties.

6. The courts hold that the finder and possessor of personal property is a _____ bailee.

7. A bailment may be terminated by operation of law if the bailed property is _____ without the fault of the bailee.

8. The common-law _____ lien arises out of a consignment transaction.
9. An _____ lien arises as the result of an enhancement of the value of a chattel by a person skilled in some kind of mechanical craft or art.
10. The person who makes a consignment is known as the _____.
11. The person to whom a consignment is made is known as the _____.
12. A _____ results when goods or property are sent by common carrier by one person in one place to another person in another place, sometimes to be sold by the latter.

True-False Questions. Indicate whether each of the following statements is true or false by circling the T or F.

T   F   1. There is no duty imposed upon the bailor to inform the bailee of hidden defects in the bailed chattel.

T   F   2. The bailee, in a bailment for the sole benefit of the bailor, is entitled to reimbursement for all necessary expenses if reasonably expended.

T   F   3. A bailment which is created for an indefinite time may be terminated without liability at the will of either the bailor or the bailee.

T   F   4. The liability of proprietors of hotels and motels for loss sustained by guests is controlled today by the statutes of the several states.

T   F   5. The unwilling possessor in an involuntary bailment cannot lawfully convert the property to his own use or refuse to redeliver it to the true owner.

T   F   6. A bailment may never be terminated by operation of law.

T   F   7. In a bailment for the sole benefit of the bailee, the bailee is not liable for any loss caused by an excessive use of the chattel.

T   F   8. In a bailment for the sole benefit of the bailor, the bailee is liable for even slight negligence.

T   F   9. The majority of the courts have held that the customer is a bailor in the safe-deposit box cases.

T   F 10. A consignee may not assert a lien against the goods in his possession.

Problems. Analyze each of the following factual situations and state your decision and the reason for your decision in the space provided.

1. The bailee rented the bailor's automobile with the understanding that the automobile would be driven to City A. The bailee, without the permission of the bailor, drove the automobile to City B, where he

stopped at a service station to refuel. During the process of refueling, lightning struck the station and ignited the gasoline, completely destroying the automobile. Is the bailor correct when he insists that the bailee must stand the loss?

_____

_____

_____

_____

_____

2. Brown, the owner of a horse stable, let Jones have one of the horses for one week to practice riding. Jones paid Brown $500 for the use of the horse. The horse became suddenly ill while in the possession of Jones, and Jones employed a veterinarian to save the life of the horse. Should Brown or should Jones pay for the services rendered by the veterinarian?

_____

_____

_____

_____

3. Aaron, under a contract of bailment, stored a box containing a collection of books with The Storage Company. Adams, a complete stranger to the employees of The Storage Company, managed to steal the books through fraudulent means. The Storage Company recovered the books, but they were badly damaged. Would The Storage Company prevail in an action against Adams to recover the damage inflicted on the books?

_____

_____

_____

_____

_____

_____

4. Brown drove his automobile to The Repair Shop for repairs. The repairs were completed, and the repairman presented a bill to Brown for $100. The Automobile Agency had a prior security interest for the payment of the purchase price of the automobile. Brown refused to pay the bill, and notified The Automobile Agency that The Repair Shop had the automobile. In a state which did not have a statute expressly making artisan's liens subordinate to prior liens, would the lien of The Repair Shop or the lien of The Automobile Agency take priority?

_____

_____

_____

_____

_____

_____

_____

_____

_____

5. Adams delivered ten sheep to Baker, who agreed to deliver ten sheep of equal value to Adams at the end of one year and in addition one pound of wool for each sheep. The ten sheep delivered by Adams were killed during a severe thunderstorm, and Baker refused to deliver any sheep to Adams at the end of the year. Is Baker under a duty to deliver ten sheep to Adams?

_____

_____

_____

_____

_____

_____

_____

_____

CHAPTER 29
DOCUMENTS OF TITLE,
CARRIERS, WAREHOUSEMEN

Chapter 29 explains in detail (1) the function of a document of title, (2) the duties and liabilities of the issuer of a document of title, (3) the negotiation and transfer of the document, and (4) the procedure for the enforcement of the lien of the carrier and the warehouseman. In studying this chapter, you must not confuse a negotiable document of title with a negotiable instrument. You must also not confuse a negotiable document with a nonnegotiable document. These distinctions are important.

Fill-in Questions. *Write the correct word or words in the blank spaces to complete the following statements.*

1. The two most common documents of title are the _____ and the _____.

2. A _____ is a person who by a warehouse receipt, bill of lading, or other document of title acknowledges possession of goods and contracts to deliver them.

3. A warehouse receipt is a receipt issued by a person engaged in the business of _____.

4. A bill of lading is a document evidencing the receipt of goods for shipment issued by a person engaged in the business of _____ and _____ goods.

5. The Code does not impose any obligation on the carrier to issue _____ bills in intrastate commerce.

6. The _____ does not generally transport the goods himself.

7. A _____ bill is a bill of lading issued at destination.

8. A bailee may deliver the goods upon a separate written authority without surrender of the document when the document is a _____ document of title.

9. The negotiable document operates in such a manner that the owner of the goods is enabled to _____ of them while they are in the possession of a _____ or warehouseman.

10. A bailee is ordinarily under a positive duty to deliver the goods only when the _____ document of title is surrendered.

11. Order bills of lading and order warehouse receipts are negotiated by _____ and _____.

12. Collecting banks and other intermediaries which transfer documents warrant only their _____ and _____.

13. The common-law rule imposes a _____ liability on a common carrier.

14. A carrier may disclaim liability by the use of words such as _____ to indicate that the goods were loaded by the shipper.

15. The strict liability of the common carrier has been diminished to some extent by the _____ clause.

True-False Questions. Indicate whether each of the following statements is true or false by circling the T or F.

T *F* 1. Documents of title are never used as a means of obtaining credit.

T *F* 2. State statutes and decisions govern the majority of warehousemen.

T *F* 3. Freight forwarders are in the business of soliciting goods in carload lots and arranging with the carrier to transport the goods in less-than-carload lots.

T *F* 4. An initial carrier is liable for wrongs committed by a connecting carrier where a through bill of lading is issued.

T *F* 5. A document of title is negotiable if its terms provide that the goods are to be delivered to bearer or to the order of bearer.

T *F* 6. When the shipper uses a negotiable bill of lading, the carrier will deliver the goods without requiring surrender of the bill of lading.

T *F* 7. A thief or finder can negotiate an order document which has been indorsed in blank.

T *F* 8. The validity of a negotiation of a document is not impaired by the fact that such a negotiation is a breach of duty on the part of the person making the negotiation.

T *F* 9. Warranties of indorsers and transferors run to the immediate purchaser only.

T *F* 10. A transferee acquires the title and rights which his transferor had or had actual authority to convey.

T *F* 11. An absolute liability is imposed on warehousemen for the

unauthorized filling in of blanks in a negotiable warehouse
receipt.

T   *F*   12.   A contract carrier, a private carrier, and a common carrier incur the identical liability.

T   *F*   13.   The liability of a warehouseman is that of an insurer of goods.

T   *F*   14.   A holder of a negotiable bill of lading is the proper party to give instructions for a diversion and reconsignment of the goods.

T   *F*   15.   The liability of a common carrier as an insurer changes to that of a warehouseman after the carrier has fulfilled the carriage contract and is holding the goods for the consignee.

Problems. *Analyze each of the following factual situations and state your decision and the reason for your decision in the space provided.*

1. Jones sold and indorsed a bill of lading with knowledge that approximately one-half of the goods represented by the bill had been destroyed by fire without fault on the part of anyone. Does the purchaser of the bill of lading have a right to recover anything from Jones?

_____

_____

_____

_____

_____

_____

_____

_____

_____

_____

_____

_____

2. Brown stored goods with a warehouseman, but no period of storage was fixed. The goods were neither perishable nor hazardous. State the circumstances under which the warehouseman may sell the goods.

_____

_____

_____

_____

_____

_____

_____

_____

_____

_____

_____

_____

_____

3. Why is it important that the consignor be permitted to obtain a destination bill in connection with shipments by air?

_____

_____

_____

_____

_____

_____

_____

_____

_____

_____

_____

_____

_____

4. A large sealed box of household goods had been shipped to Brown. Brown delivered the sealed box to a warehouse and received a negotiable warehouse receipt. Brown desired to take delivery of the box, but he had inadvertently destroyed the warehouse receipt. The warehouseman, therefore, refused to deliver the sealed box to Brown. What remedy, if any, is available to Brown?

_____

_____

_____

_____

_____

_____

_____

_____

_____

5. The Smiths, who were moving from Illinois to Texas, employed The Transfer and Storage Company to move their household furniture. The furniture was transported and delivered to the residence of the Smiths. The Smiths failed to pay the cost of transportation, and The Transfer and Storage Company claimed to have a lien on the furniture for the cost of transportation. Decide.

_____

_____

_____

_____

_____

_____

_____

_____

_____

6. Explain how the warehouseman may terminate and enforce the lien when the goods are hazardous.

_____
_____
_____
_____
_____
_____
_____
_____
_____
_____

7. Brown stored certain goods in a warehouse in April, and the warehouseman voluntarily surrendered the goods to Brown in May without collecting the charges. In June, Brown stored other goods in the same warehouse. In July, Brown asked the warehouseman to again surrender the goods without collecting the charges, but the warehouseman refused. Brown paid the charges for the goods stored during the month of June, but the warehouseman refused to deliver the goods unless Brown also paid the charges for the goods stored during the month of April. Was this action of the warehouseman justified?

_____
_____
_____
_____
_____
_____
_____
_____
_____
_____

8. Brown stored certain fungible grain with a warehouseman-dealer and received a negotiable warehouse receipt, which he negotiated to Jones. The warehouseman, who was in the business of buying and selling fungible grain, thereafter sold the grain stored by Brown to Smith, a buyer in the ordinary course of business. The warehouseman then become insolvent. Will Jones be able to recover his grain from Smith?

_____

_____

_____

_____

_____

_____

_____

_____

_____

_____

9. Enumerate the five exceptions to the common-law rule of a strict liability imposed on the common carrier.

_____

_____

_____

_____

_____

_____

_____

_____

_____

_____

10. Enumerate the excuses that may be offered by a carrier and a warehouseman for nondelivery of the goods to the person entitled to delivery.

_____

_____

_____

_____

_____

_____

_____

_____

_____

_____

_____

SECURED TRANSACTIONS   6

CHAPTER 30
SECURED TRANSACTIONS:
INTRODUCTION

Chapter 30 is not difficult to understand, but it contains words and definitions that must be memorized. Learning this new vocabulary is essential; otherwise you will find the next two chapters difficult to understand. The fill-in questions are designed to aid the student in this tedious process.

Fill-in Questions. *Write the correct word or words in the blank spaces to complete the following statements.*

1. Goods are _____ if they are used or bought for use primarily for personal, family, or household purposes.
2. Goods are _____ if they are used or bought for use primarily in business, including farming, a profession, a nonprofit organization, or a governmental agency.
3. Goods are _____ only if they are in the possession of a debtor engaged in raising, fattening, or grazing livestock, or other farm operations.
4. Goods are classified as _____ if they are held for immediate or ultimate sale in the ordinary course of business.
5. The definition of _____ includes a right to payment for goods sold or leased, or for services rendered, which right to payment is not evidenced by an instrument or chattel paper.
6. An _____ is any right to payment under a contract not yet earned by performance, which right to payment is not evidenced by an instrument or chattel paper.
7. The definition of _____ includes intangibles which do not fall within the definition of the other five kinds of intangibles.
8. The word _____ includes the bill of lading, dock warrant, dock receipt, warehouse receipt, delivery orders, and the like.
9. The word _____ includes negotiable instruments and investment securities.

10. The words _____ include a writing or writings which evidence both a monetary obligation and a security interest in or lease of specific goods.

11. In a secured transaction, the person having the security is called the _____; the person giving the security is called the _____; the property is called the _____; the agreement is called the _____; and the interest is called the _____.

True-False Questions. Indicate whether each of the following statements is true or false by circling the T or F.

T F 1. The Code abolishes the use of conditional sales and chattel mortgages in secured transactions.

T F 2. Tangible personal property has a physical existence, such as automobiles, jewelry, and the like.

T F 3. The Code calls tangible personal property "goods."

T F 4. Intangible personal property has no physical existence, but is only a right to receive property.

T F 5. The definition of accounts refers to earned and unearned accounts receivable.

T F 6. Oral contracts for the sale of general intangibles for a price beyond $5,000 are not enforceable.

T F 7. Eggs held by the farmer-producer for sale are "farm products."

T F 8. Eggs on the shelves of a supermarket are "inventory."

T F 9. A note, check, or draft is a "document of title."

T F 10. A bill of lading or a warehouse receipt is an "instrument."

T F 11. As a general rule, a document must purport to be issued by or addressed to a bailee.

T F 12. An owner who is not a warehouseman may issue a receipt which will be given the effect of a warehouse receipt if such receipt is issued for distilled spirits or agricultural commodities where a bond is required by statute or the withdrawal of such goods or if a license is required for the issuance of such receipt.

T F 13. In a transaction which is evidenced both by a security agreement or a lease and by an instrument or a series of instruments, the group of writings taken together constitutes chattel paper.

T F 14. Article 9, "Secured Transactions," applies to any transaction, irrespective of its form, if it is intended to create a security interest in personal property or fixtures and the sale of accounts or chattel paper.

CHAPTER 31
THE SECURITY INTEREST

You may need to review the definitions that were given in the last chapter before proceeding with the study of Chapter 31. This chapter also introduces you to some new vocabulary, which must be understood. This chapter (1) explains the requirements necessary to create a valid security agreement, (2) describes the meaning of attachment and explains the attachment of the security interest, (3) states the methods of perfecting the security interest, and (4) discusses the rights and duties of the parties when the secured party and when the debtor are each in possession of the collateral.

Fill-in Questions. *Write the correct word or words in the blank spaces to complete the following statements.*

1. The word _____ relates to the coming into existence of the security interest.
2. The word _____ relates to taking the security into possession or to filing a financing statement to make the security interest effective against third persons.
3. The form of filing prescribed by the Code is termed _____.
4. Some states have enacted statutes which require a security interest to be perfected by local and _____ filing.
5. The principal method of perfecting the security interest of the secured party is by filing a _____.
6. The word _____ is defined to include whatever is received when collateral or proceeds is sold, exchanged, collected, or otherwise disposed of.
7. A _____ is a demand, time, savings, passbook, or like account maintained with a bank, savings and loan association, credit union, or like organization, other than an account evidenced by a certificate of deposit.
8. The duration of the perfection by filing is effective for a period of _____ after the date of filing.
9. The basic rule is that the governing law of the perfection of a security interest in "ordinary goods" is the law of the jurisdiction where the

collateral is located when the _____ occurs for the perfection of the security interest.

10. Perfection of a security interest in documents and instruments is governed by the _____ rule.

11. Perfection in an account, general intangibles, and mobile goods, such as rental cars, trailers, and road-building machinery, will be governed by the law of the jurisdiction where the _____ is located.

True-False Questions. *Indicate whether each of the following statements is true or false by circling the T or F.*

T   F   1. The secured party will lose his security interest if he does not exercise reasonable care in preserving the collateral in his possession.

T   F   2. When the financing arrangement has been terminated with respect to consumer goods, the secured party must file a termination statement within one month.

T   F   3. A properly signed continuation statement must be filed when the secured party assigns a perfected security interest.

T   F   4. A financing statement is a form prepared and filed in a designated public office in order to notify third persons that the debtor and the creditor are going to be engaged in financing.

T   F   5. A security interest in instruments may be perfected only by possession.

T   F   6. A security interest in instruments and negotiable documents is perfected by attachment alone for a period of twenty-one days without filing or possession.

T   F   7. Perfection of accounts and general intangibles may be accomplished by taking possession or by filing a financing statement.

T   F   8. Perfection in "goods" may be accomplished only by filing.

T   F   9. A security interest means an interest in personal property which secures the payment of money or performance of an obligation.

T   F   10. The security agreement must always be in writing.

T   F   11. Filing of the financing statement may be local, central, or dual.

T   F   12. A carbon, photographic, or other reproduction of the financing statement or the security agreement cannot be filed as a financing statement.

T   F   13. A financing statement, in case of a partnership debtor, must contain both the name of the partnership and the individual names of the partners.

T   F   14. A signature by the secured party is not required in a financing statement, but the signature of the secured party alone will suffice when the original statement lapsed because no continuation statement was filed.

T *F* 15. The duration of perfection of a real estate mortgage which is filed as a "fixture filing" will not terminate until the mortgage is terminated by being released, satisfied of record, foreclosed, or the like.

T *F* 16. The financing statement, in case of growing crops or crops to be grown, must be filed in the real estate records in the county where the crops are growing or are to be grown and in the real estate records of the county where the farmer resides if the two places are located in different counties.

T *F* 17. Perfection of a security interest in documents and instruments will be governed by the law of the jurisdiction where the last event occurs for the perfection of the security interest.

Problems. Analyze each of the following factual situations and state your decision and the reason for your decision in the space provided.

1. The Florist Shop borrowed $10,000 from the First Bank, and the inventory of The Florist Shop was used as collateral for the loan. The First Bank perfected its security interest by filing a financing statement. The inventory was damaged by fire, and The Insurance Company paid The Florist Shop $3,000 for the loss. The First Bank contended that the proceeds of the insurance—the $3,000—was proceeds. Do you agree with this contention?

_____

_____

_____

_____

_____

_____

2. Brown and The Finance Company entered into a security agreement whereby Brown borrowed $5,000 from The Finance Company. The financing statement contained a description of the collateral by item, the name of The Finance Company, and the signature and address

of Brown. Does the financing statement comply with the formal requisites of a financing statement?

_____

_____

_____

_____

_____

3. Aaron and Adams both had a security interest in the inventory of The Hardware Company. Aaron properly filed a financing statement on January 1, 1965, and Adams properly filed a financing statement on June 1, 1965. On May 1, 1970, both Aaron and Adams claimed to have a priority in the inventory of The Hardware Company. Who is correct?

_____

_____

_____

_____

_____

_____

_____

4. The Jewelry Company borrowed $10,000 from the First Bank and gave the First Bank a security interest in the inventory of The Jewelry Company as collateral for the loan. A financing statement was properly filed. The creditors of The Jewelry Company contended that the security interest was fraudulent against creditors, because the debtor had complete control over the collateral. Do you agree with this contention?

_____

_____

_____

_____

_____

_____

_____

_____

_____

5. Smith purchased and installed a new furnace in his home and executed a real estate mortgage which was properly filed on November 1, 1968, as a fixture filing by the Acme Company, the secured party. On May 1, 1974, the Sunshine Company was considering a loan to Smith to be secured by a real estate mortgage on the home of Smith. If the loan is approved and secured by a real estate mortgage, will the Sunshine Company have priority over the Acme Company?

_____

_____

_____

_____

_____

_____

_____

CHAPTER 32
PRIORITIES AND REMEDIES

Chapter 32 is the most detailed and is probably the most difficult of the three chapters on secured trans-actions. You should, therefore, be prepared to spend more time studying this chapter. Explained in this chapter are (1) the details of the priorities among the conflicting interest in (a) proceeds, (b) future advances, and (c) fixtures, (2) the rights of the secured party in the collateral after the default of the debtor, and (3) the remedy of the debtor, or any other person adversely affected, when the secured party is proceeding in a contrary manner relating to default.

Fill-in Questions. Write the correct word or words in the blank spaces to complete the following statements.

1. A _____ creditor is one who acquires a lien on the property in question by attachment, levy, or the like.
2. An _____ lien is a lien securing a claim arising from work which enhances or preserves the value of the collateral.
3. A _____ security interest will arise when a seller sells goods to the buyer and retains a security interest in the goods.
4. A new engine installed in an old automobile is a good example of an _____.
5. A fixture filing must occur in the office where the records pertaining to _____ are recorded or filed.
6. Money, checks, deposit accounts, and the like are _____ _____ proceeds, and all other proceeds are _____ proceeds.
7. The debtor is neither entitled to any _____ nor liable for any _____, unless the security agreement so provides, where the underlying transaction involved the sale of accounts or chattel paper rather than a secured transaction.
8. The secured party must act in a manner which is _____ reasonable in disposing of the collateral upon the default of the debtor.
9. The priority of perfected security interests will be determined by the _____ of filing or perfection.

10. The effect of the rules of law in Article 9 of the Uniform Commercial Code is to give a purchase-money security interest priority over an _____ security interest.

11. A purchase-money security interest in collateral other than inventory is given priority over a conflicting security interest if the security interest is perfected at the time the debtor receives possession of the collateral or within _____ days thereafter.

12. A perfected purchase-money security interest in inventory carries over only to _____ proceeds.

13. Goods are _____ when they become so related to particular real estate that an interest in them arises under real estate law.

14. A _____ filing is designed to give the fixture secured party priority over real estate parties, such as real estate mortgagees and the like.

15. A fixture filing must occur in the office where the records pertaining to _____ are recorded or filed.

16. A secured party can achieve priority over an existing mortgage or other encumbrance only by means of a _____ security interest unless the prior encumbrancer waives his interest in the fixture in writing.

True-False Questions. Indicate whether each of the following statements is true or false by circling the T or F.

T   *F*   1.   The priority of perfected security interests will be determined by the time of filing or perfection.

T   *F*   2.   The Code provides that a prior security interest takes priority only when a statute expressly makes an artisan's lien subordinate.

T   *F*   3.   As against bulk purchasers and lien creditors, the purchase-money security interest in collateral other than inventory is perfected for ten days from the date the secured party advanced value.

T   *F*   4.   A secured party loses his perfected security interest in proceeds when the debtor is involved in insolvency proceedings.

T   *F*   5.   A fixture cannot be removed by anyone having an interest in the fixture if substantial damage is done to the premises by such removal.

T   *F*   6.   A secured party may not take possession of collateral on default of the debtor without judicial process.

T   *F*   7.   The secured party has the right after default to collect claims due the debtor from third persons.

T   *F*   8.   When the secured party is proceeding in a contrary manner relating to default, the debtor may obtain an order of the court ordering the secured party to dispose of the collateral, or he may obtain an order to restrain disposition of the collateral.

T   *F*   9.   The debtor may not redeem the collateral after the secured party takes possession upon default of the debtor.

T   *F*   10.   An unperfected security interest is subordinate to the rights of a lien creditor who became such lien creditor before the security interest is perfected.

T   *F*   11.   As a general rule, a secured party does not have a permanently perfected security interest in proceeds unless there is a specific claim made in the financing statement to such proceeds.

T   *F*   12.   A secured party will have a permanently perfected security interest in proceeds consisting of negotiable notes as a result of filing the financing statement only.

T   *F*   13.   A secured party will not lose his priority when he makes a future advance to the debtor with knowledge that the debtor had sold the collateral not in the regular course of business forty-six days prior to the future advance.

T   *F*   14.   The law of the specific state will determine whether lumber, bricks, and the like incorporated in a building upon the land is or is not a fixture.

T   *F*   15.   A construction mortgage which is properly filed or recorded will have priority over a purchase-money seller of goods installed as a part of the original construction.

T   *F*   16.   The Code does not abandon, in any event, the "material injury to the freehold" rule.

T   *F*   17.   A person who buys minerals, oil, and gas at the wellhead or minehead may qualify as a buyer in the ordinary course of business.

T   *F*   18.   A purchaser who purchases farm products from a person engaged in farming operations is a buyer in the ordinary course of business.

T   *F*   19.   A secured party who has a perfected security interest in proceeds will continue to have a perfected security interest in the proceeds whenever the debtor is involved in insolvency proceedings with respect to identifiable cash proceeds in the form of money which is not commingled with other money nor deposited in a deposit account prior to the insolvency proceedings.

T   *F*   20.   A secured party, upon the default of the debtor, is compelled to dispose of the collateral—to sell or lease or otherwise dispose of the collateral—if the secured transaction involves consumer goods and the debtor has paid 50 percent of the purchase price on a purchase-money security interest.

Problems. Analyze each of the following factual situations and state your decision and the reason for your decision in the space provided.

1. Enumerate the three instances when a purchase-money security interest will arise.

_____

_____

_____

_____

_____

_____

2. The First Bank financed the inventory of The Office Supply, and filed a financing statement in which the chattel paper proceeds was claimed. The chattel paper, however, was left in the possession of The Office Supply. The Office Supply thereafter sold three executive desks to Davis under an installment sales agreement, and the resulting chattel paper was assigned to the Second Bank. The Second Bank, however, loaned $1,000 to The Office Supply and took possession of the chattel paper in the ordinary course of business. Does the First Bank or the Second Bank have priority in the proceeds of the chattel paper?

_____

_____

_____

_____

3. A merchant whose inventory was being financed by the First Bank sold certain specific goods to Barsh. The specific goods were returned and were later resold to Brown, a buyer in the ordinary course of business. The security interest of the First Bank had been perfected by filing. Is the First Bank entitled to a security interest in the goods sold to Brown?

_____

_____

_____

_____

_____

4. The Motel and The Furniture Company entered into a security agreement whereby The Furniture Company sold certain furniture to The Motel, and the agreement contained a clause encumbering the furniture and all after-acquired furniture. The Furniture Company perfected its security interest by filing a financing statement. Brown, another furniture dealer, thereafter sold certain furniture to The Motel and retained a security interest in the furniture. Brown perfected his security interest in the furniture by filing a financing statement five days after The Motel took possession of the furniture. Does the security interest of The Furniture Company take priority over the security interest of Brown?

_____

_____

_____

_____

_____

_____

_____

5. Explain how a receivables financer may protect his security interest in chattel paper or instruments, i.e., the collateral, when the collateral is left in the possession of the debtor.

_____

_____

_____

_____

_____

6. In the case of consumer goods, explain the duties of the secured party when he chooses to retain the collateral after default of the debtor.

AGENCY 7

CHAPTER 33
CREATION AND AUTHORITY

You should have little difficulty with this chapter and the remaining three chapters devoted to the law of agency. These chapters do not have two sets of rules, as was found in several of the chapters devoted to the laws of contracts. Chapter 33 explains the distinction between agents and similar relationships, and this distinction should be kept in mind along with the distinction between the various kinds of agents. You should learn (1) the methods by which an agency may be created other than by appointment, (2) the various kinds of authority an agent may have, and (3) the rights acquired by and duties imposed upon the principal by ratification.

Fill-in Questions. *Write the correct word or words in the blank spaces to complete the following statements.*

1. An _____ is a person who contracts to do a piece of work according to his own judgment and methods.
2. An _____ is a person authorized to create, modify, or terminate contractual relations in behalf of the principal.
3. A _____ is an agent employed to sell merchandise consigned to him for that purpose.
4. A good illustration of an agency by _____ is when an emergency or disaster occurs during an ocean voyage.
5. _____ authority may be delegated to an agent expressly or impliedly.
6. Implied, or _____, authority is actual authority which arises from the words or acts of the principal and from the facts and circumstances of the case.
7. The person holding a power of attorney is known as an _____.
8. An agency by _____ arises when a state statute provides that a service of process may be made upon the secretary of state in lieu of a nonresident motorist.
9. Apparent, or _____, authority is that authority

which the principal permits the agent to exercise or which he holds the agent out as having although such authority has not been delegated to the agent.

10. An agency by _____ may be created when one person voluntarily or negligently permits another person to conduct himself in such a manner that a third person is led to believe that an agency relationship has been created.

11. An agency relationship between the principal and a _____ agent may be created by an agreement unsupported by consideration.

12. A _____ agent usually has wide general authority to act for his principal.

13. An agent authorized to sell an automobile is a _____ agent.

14. A factor who sells merchandise on credit for an additional commission and guarantees the solvency of the purchaser and his performance of the contract is known as a _____ agent.

15. _____ is the subsequent acceptance or approval by one person of an unauthorized act of another person.

16. The dual agency of an auctioneer is for the purpose of _____.

True-False Questions. Indicate whether each of the following statements is true or false by circling the T or F.

T   *F*   1. Ordinarily, an employer is liable for the torts committed by an independent contractor.

T   *F*   2. Many of the rules of the law of agency are as applicable to an employee as they are to an agent.

T   *F*   3. A general manager of a department store is an illustration of a special agent.

T   *F*   4. Professional agents do not have the authority to enter into contractual relations with third persons in behalf of their principal.

T   *F*   5. A factor is frequently referred to as a commission merchant.

T   *F*   6. A principal should repudiate an unauthorized act promptly after receiving information of the transaction in order to avoid liability resulting from the unauthorized act on the basis of ratification.

T   *F*   7. The primary function of a broker is to act as an intermediary between two other parties.

T   *F*   8. A principal will be bound by ratification if he deliberately and expressly ratifies the act knowing that his information is incomplete.

T   *F*   9. Ratification relates back and becomes effective as of the date the act was performed by the agent except for intervening rights of third persons.

T *F* 10. The appointment of an agent must always be in writing.

T *F* 11. Corporations do not have the capacity to appoint agents.

T *F* 12. Ratification is approval after conduct.

Problems. *Analyze each of the following factual situations and state your decision and the reason for your decision in the space provided.*

1. Baker, who employed Hipp to purchase a used automobile, instructed Hipp that the automobile was to be in good condition but that the purchase price of the automobile should not be more than $1,200. Is Hipp an agent, a servant, or an independent contractor?

_____

_____

_____

_____

_____

2. Brent, the manager of a large department store, was permitted to draw checks on the account of the store and to sign them in the following manner: "Wilson's Department Store, by Thomas L. Brent." He drew a check on the account of the department store and appropriated the proceeds to his own personal use. The department store now seeks to recover the amount of this check from the bank. Is the department store estopped from denying Brent's authority?

_____

_____

_____

_____

_____

3. Myers, twenty years of age, appointed James, twenty-two years of age, his agent for the purpose of purchasing a motorcycle. Myers provided James with the cash with which to make the purchase. Two weeks after the sale was consummated, Myers returned the motorcycle to Davis, from whom it was purchased. Davis refused to agree to the attempted rescission, or disaffirmance, by Myers and contended

that since James was an adult Myers could not disaffirm the sale. Do you agree with this contention?

_____

_____

_____

_____

_____

_____

4. Jones, an agent of Williams, exceeded his authority by purchasing in his own name a refrigerator. When Williams learned of the purchase, he stated that he ratified it. Williams, before the seller of the refrigerator had acted further, repudiated the transaction. Is the seller of the refrigerator correct when he argues that Williams cannot repudiate his ratification?

_____

_____

_____

_____

_____

_____

5. Paul owed Thomas $500 on a gambling debt in a state where gambling is absolutely void. Thomas demanded that Adams, Paul's agent, give Thomas a promissory note in payment of the debt. Paul thereafter attempted to ratify the unauthorized act of Adams. Is Paul liable on the note?

_____

_____

_____

_____

_____

_____

CHAPTER 34
PRINCIPAL AND
THIRD PERSON

The aim of Chapter 34 is (1) to point out those acts which are within the course and scope of the authority of the agent; (2) to explain the rights and liabilities of the third person, the agent, and the disclosed and undisclosed principal; and (3) to examine some specific tortious and criminal acts of the agent that will impose liability on the principal.

Fill-in Questions. *Write the correct word or words in the blank spaces to complete the following statements.*

1. An agent who has been authorized to buy goods for his principal has the _____ authority to buy on credit if his principal has not provided the agent with funds.

2. An agent who has authority to collect the purchase price for goods ordinarily has authority to collect in _____ only.

3. The professional broker or real estate agent, as a general rule, has performed his duty when he has found a purchaser who is _____ to purchase upon the terms specified.

4. An _____ principal is one who is represented by an agent who does not reveal the fact that he is acting in a representative capacity.

5. A _____ principal is one whose existence and identity are known to the third person.

6. An agent may employ other persons to assist him in the purely _____ or _____ details of his duty.

7. The _____ cases provide much of the litigation concerning negligence of the agent when the principal attempts to show that the agent was not acting within the scope of his employment.

8. The significance of the relation between the principal and the third person is that the principal is bound by, and liable for, those acts which the agent does within the _____.

True-False Questions. Indicate whether each of the following statements is true or false by circling the T or F.

T   F   1. Possession alone of personal property confers authority upon an agent to sell the property.

T   F   2. Authority to purchase will be implied if the principal has held the agent out as having such authority.

T   F   3. A third person who contracts with the agent of a partially disclosed principal can never enforce the contract against the principal.

T   F   4. An agent of an undisclosed principal can have no apparent authority.

T   F   5. An undisclosed principal cannot enforce a contract which involves personal services.

T   F   6. An agent, in the absence of the express or implied consent of his principal, cannot generally delegate his authority to a subagent.

T   F   7. The principal is never liable for crimes committed by his agent.

T   F   8. The principal can escape liability merely because the act causing a tort was done by the agent willfully.

Problems. Analyze each of the following factual situations and state your decision and the reason for your decision in the space provided.

1. Baxter was the general manager of a large department store. Jones, who worked in the shoe department as a salesman, became ill. He was, therefore, compelled to leave his job. Baxter immediately employed Reeves to fill the vacancy. Does Baxter have authority to appoint Reeves as an agent of the department store, which store is a corporation?

_____

_____

_____

_____

_____

_____

_____

_____

2. The Acme Department Store employed Bridges as a clerk during the months of November and December. It was his duty to assist prospective customers in effecting sales. The customers were expected to pay for the merchandise at a check-out place, which was clearly visible. Bridges succeeded in selling Stone a watch for $200. Stone insisted that he should deliver the money to Bridges. Bridges accepted the money and immediately absconded. The management refused to allow Stone to keep the watch unless he paid for it at the check-out place, but Stone insisted that he had already paid for the watch. Is Stone correct?

_____

_____

_____

_____

_____

_____

_____

3. The X Corporation sold a large oven to a bakery shop, and B. B. Brown signed a promissory note in payment of the oven as follows: "B. B. Brown." The note was not paid on its maturity date, and The X Corporation brought an action against B. B. Brown to recover the amount of the note. The defense of B. B. Brown was that the bakery shop was owned by Jones and that he signed the note as agent for Jones. Is this a good defense?

_____

_____

_____

_____

_____

_____

_____

4. The agent-manager of a business wrote a libelous letter in which he attacked the credit of a competitor in an effort to obtain a contract in behalf of his principal. Is the principal correct when he argues that he is not liable for this wrongful act of the agent?

_____

_____

_____

_____

_____

_____

_____

_____

_____

5. The agent was a traveling salesman with authority to solicit orders and transmit them to the home office for acceptance or rejection. The defendant, a retailer, had placed many orders with the agent in the past. After such orders were accepted and the goods delivered, the defendant always mailed the money to the principal. On one occasion, however, the agent requested and received five new suits in payment. The orders were filled and delivered, but the defendant claims that he has already paid. Is the defendant liable?

_____

_____

_____

_____

_____

_____

_____

_____

CHAPTER 35
AGENT AND THIRD PERSON

*Chapter 35, which deals with the relationship between
the agent and the third person, is neither difficult nor
very long. You will learn that an agent may create a
personal liability to the third person; this liability may
arise out of both contracts and torts. You will also
learn that the third person may find himself liable to
the agent personally, and this liability may also arise
out of both contracts and torts.*

Fill-in Questions. *Write the correct word or words in the blank spaces to
complete the following statements.*

1. An agent who assumes to contract in the name of an _____
    or _____ principal renders himself liable to
    third persons.
2. An agent may find himself _____ liable to the
    third person if the agent carelessly executes a written agreement.
3. An agent who signs a writing within the course and scope of his
    authority has no _____ on the instrument if
    he names his principal and expresses by appropriate words that the
    writing is that of the principal.
4. An agent who expressly represents that he is authorized to enter into
    a contract for a principal, knowing full well that he has no such au-
    thority, is liable in tort in an action for _____.
5. The principal and the agent are _____ and
    _____ liable for the torts of the agent com-
    mitted within the course and scope of the employment.
6. An agent who acts in good faith and honestly believes that he has the
    authority which he assumes to exercise, but who has no such authority,
    is liable upon an _____ of authority.
7. A factor or an auctioneer who sues for and receives the purchase price
    of goods sold holds the proceeds in a _____ or
    trust capacity for his principal.
8. An agent who commits a _____ while follow-
    ing the principal's instructions is nevertheless liable.
9. The agent of an _____ principal always binds
    himself and has the right to sue the third person in his own name in
    the event of nonperformance by the third person.
10. The agent may bring an action to recover damages for his personal

injuries caused by the _____ acts of **third** persons.

11. The older cases hold that such words as "agent," "agt.," or "trustee" were _____.

12. A factor selling under a _____ commission may sue for the purchase price in the event of default by the buyer.

True-False Questions. *Indicate whether each of the following statements is true or false by circling the T or F.*

T   F   1. The agent may never bring an action to recover damages for his personal injuries caused by the tortious acts of a third person.

T   F   2. The agent is not personally liable to third persons for his torts.

T   F   3. The agent is not personally liable to third persons unless he intentionally assumes the liability.

T   F   4. It is clear that a duly authorized agent who contracts in the name of another person creates a personal liability of the agent.

T   F   5. An agent who intentionally misrepresents or conceals his principal's incapacity is personally liable.

T   F   6. A third person who induces a principal to discharge his agent without justification is liable in damages to the agent so discharged.

Problems. *Analyze each of the following factual situations and state your decision and the reason for your decision in the space provided.*

1. The agent, who had authority to sell his principal's goods, agreed to be personally liable for the purchase price of all goods sold. The agent was to receive a higher than usual commission. The third person, after buying and receiving such goods from the agent, refused to pay for them. Does the agent have a right to sue the third person in his own name?

_____

_____

_____

_____

_____

_____

_____

2. The agent was authorized by his principal, a farmer, to sell some vegetables to The Farmers Market. The agent sold the vegetables, and The Farmers Market paid a part of the purchase price directly to the farmer. The vegetables were deteriorated and below the customary quality. The Farmers Market thereupon brought an action against the agent. Should The Farmers Market recover?

_____

_____

_____

_____

_____

_____

_____

_____

_____

3. The agent was authorized to sell corporate stock of a certain corporation, his principal. The agent by means of fraudulent representations sold stock to a third person and received the money which was paid over to his principal. The agent received no direct benefit from this transaction. Does the third person have a right to recover the money from the agent?

_____

_____

_____

_____

_____

_____

_____

_____

4. An agent of a building contractor purchased some cabinets from Brown to be used in an apartment building. Brown would not extend credit to the contractor. The cabinets were sold and delivered, however, to the contractor with the understanding that the credit was extended to the agent. Is the agent personally liable for the purchase price of the cabinets?

_____

_____

_____

_____

_____

_____

_____

_____

_____

_____

CHAPTER 36
PRINCIPAL AND AGENT

Chapters 33, 34, and 35 were devoted to the creation of the agency, the authority of the agent, the relationship between the principal and the third person, and the relationship between the agent and the third person. Chapter 36 concludes the law of agency, and is devoted to (1) the duties and liabilities of the agent, (2) the duties and liabilities of the principal, and (3) the termination of the agency.

Fill-in Questions. Write the correct word or words in the blank spaces to complete the following statements.

1. Two well-recognized rights which the agent possesses against the principal are reimbursement and _____.

2. An agency coupled with an _____ will not be terminated by the death of the principal, but an agency given as _____ will be terminated by the death of the principal.

3. The principal, upon termination of the authority of a general agent, should give _____ notice to those persons— although they never dealt with the agent prior to the revocation of the agency—who are justified in believing the agency continues to exist.

4. The principal, upon termination of the authority of a general agent, should give _____ notice to all persons who have had dealings with the agent.

5. An agent may act in a _____ provided both principals have been duly informed of the dual role of the agent and have consented to it.

6. An agent may make a departure from the instructions of his principal if a _____ arises which will not admit of delay for communication with the principal.

7. The courts, in the absence of a specific agreement, treat a drawing _____ as a minimum salary.

8. An agent is under a duty not to divulge _____ information.

9. An agent is under a duty not to disclose _____ communications to his principal.

10. A distinction is made in many states between an _____ right to sell and an _____ agency.

11. An agency which contains no provision for its duration nor anything to indicate that it is to continue for a certain period of time is known as an agency at _____.

True-False Questions. Indicate whether each of the following statements is true or false by circling the T or F.

T *F* 1. General information and ordinary experience of an agent are quite distinct from secret information.

T *F* 2. Knowledge is imputed to the principal even though the agent was acting for his own secret gain.

T *F* 3. A traveling agent, in the absence of an agreement to the contrary, is entitled to his commission on all orders from his territory which are accepted by the principal.

T *F* 4. A broker is never authorized to effect contracts on behalf of his principal.

T *F* 5. The principal and agent may put an end to the agency by mutual consent at any time.

T *F* 6. The general rule is that the death of the principal will not terminate the agency.

T *F* 7. Bankruptcy of the agent terminates the authority of the agent to receive money and to perform acts of a like nature.

T *F* 8. There is no distinction between an agency coupled with an interest and an agency given as security.

Problems. Analyze each of the following factual situations and state your decision and the reason for your decision in the space provided.

1. The agent was employed to collect payments due on installment sales. The principal, for good cause, revoked the agent's authority but failed to notify the third person of the revocation. Subsequent to his dismissal, the former agent collected $100 from the third person who had no knowledge that the agency had been terminated. The former agent absconded with the money so collected. Can the principal recover the $100 from the third person?

_____

_____

_____

_____

_____

_____

2. The principal appointed Brown as his agent to solicit orders for magazines and transmit the orders to the principal for approval. The principal and Brown, however, did not agree on the compensation to be paid Brown. What amount will Brown be able to recover for his services?

_____

_____

_____

_____

_____

_____

_____

_____

_____

3. The principal and the agent entered into an agency agreement on January 1, 1970, and the agency was to last for two years. The principal decided he would prefer to have his son perform the duties being performed by the agent. The principal, therefore, wrongfully discharged the agent on February 1, 1970. What remedy, if any, is available to the agent?

_____

_____

_____

_____

_____

_____

_____

_____

_____

4. The agent was authorized to collect rents from various tenants of the principal. The principal was judicially declared insane, and the court appointed Davis as the guardian of the principal. The agent continued to collect rents for the principal and absconded with the money. Would Davis prevail in an action against the tenants to compel the tenants to pay the money collected by the agent twice?

_____

_____

_____

_____

_____

_____

_____

_____

_____

5. Mary, who had been the bookkeeper for The Jewelry Store for five years, resigned. She went into the jewelry business for herself soon thereafter and used a list of the customers of The Jewelry Store in soliciting customers for her new business. The Jewelry Store asked the court for an injunction to restrain Mary from using the list of customers taken from The Jewelry Store in order to solicit customers for her new business. Should the injunction be granted?

_____

_____

_____

_____

_____

_____

_____

_____

BUSINESS ORGANIZATIONS 8

CHAPTER 37
PARTNERSHIP: NATURE,
CREATION, PROPERTY

Chapter 37 is the first of four chapters explaining the law of partnership, and the Uniform Partnership Act is used as a basis for the material presented in the chapters. This chapter is devoted to (1) the kinds of partnerships and the kinds of partners, (2) the formalities of the formation of a partnership, (3) the essential elements of a partnership, (4) the property which is classified as partnership property, and (5) when the title to partnership property may be held in the partnership name.

Fill-in Questions. *Write the correct word or words in the blank spaces to complete the following statements.*

1. Partners who are not known to the public as such and who take no active part in the management of the business are known as _____ partners.

2. A common purpose for which a _____ is created is to buy specific real estate with the expectation of reselling it at a profit.

3. Persons who appear to the public as partners, but who are not actually partners, are referred to as _____ partners.

4. The classification of partnerships as _____ and _____ is used to distinguish the so-called commercial partnership from the professional partnership.

5. Partners are classified as _____ and _____ partners in connection with the statutory limited partnership.

6. The courts are fairly agreed that the parties have formed a partnership _____ if, in pursuance of an oral agreement, the partnership business is carried on.

7. The restrictions which the common law places on the partnership with the respect to holding title to real property have never been applied to _____ property.

8. The words _____ are quite generally said to mean expectation of continued public patronage.

9. The term _____ is broad enough to embrace everything that the partnership owns.

10. Most of the states have enacted _____ name statutes.

True-False Questions. Indicate whether each of the following statements is true or false by circling the T or F.

T   *F*   1. The professional partnerships are classified as trading partnerships.

T   *F*   2. The vast majority of agreements to form a partnership are equally valid whether oral or written.

T   *F*   3. The Partnership Act provides that an agreement to form a partnership for a period of more than one year must be in writing to be enforceable.

T   *F*   4. An agreement to form a partnership for the purpose of subdividing a tract of land into lots is required to be in writing to be enforceable.

T   *F*   5. The provisions in a written partnership agreement will vary with the nature of the business.

T   *F*   6. Partnerships that buy and sell, building and plumbing contractors, manufacturers, and similar commercial businesses are classified as trading partnerships.

T   *F*   7. It is essential to the existence of a partnership that a firm name be adopted.

T   *F*   8. A partnership cannot adopt a name so much like a name already in use as to mislead the public.

T   *F*   9. Partners are prohibited by statute from using a fictitious name as a partnership name.

T   *F*   10. Corporations and insane persons are prohibited by statute from becoming a member of a partnership.

Problems. Analyze each of the following factual situations and state your decision and the reason for your decision in the space provided.

1. Brown and Jones entered into an oral agreement which provided that for a term of five years they were to conduct a plumbing business for profit. The agreement further provided that Brown was to do all the work in connection with the business and that Jones, who owned the building in which the business was to be carried on, was to supply the space for the business free of rent, was to furnish a truck for the business, and was to pay for the water and electricity used, and that Brown and Jones were to share equally in the profits. Is this a partnership?

_____

_____

_____

_____

_____

_____

_____

_____

2. Aaron and Adams formed a partnership, and Aaron made a loan of $40,000 to the partnership. Aaron also permitted $40,000, his share of the profits, to accumulate in the partnership business. Differences arose between Aaron and Adams, and Adams contended that the $80,000 was partnership capital. Do you agree with this contention?

_____

_____

_____

_____

_____

_____

_____

3. Brown, Jones, and Smith entered into an agreement whereby they were to be the owners and operators of a summer camp for boys. They also agreed that all of the profits made from the camp would be donated to the Boy Scouts of America. Is this a partnership?

_____

_____

_____

_____

_____

_____

_____

4. Martin, Lewis, and Clark formed a partnership for the purpose of carrying on the business of growing and selling ornamental shrubbery. Martin and Lewis contributed $30,000 each, and Clark gave the partnership the use of forty acres of land that he owned. The partnership thereafter become insolvent. The creditors of the partnership and the individual creditors of Clark both contend that they have a prior claim to the land. Discuss this contention.

_____

_____

_____

_____

_____

_____

_____

_____

5. Robert Brown, a partner in the firm of Brown & Smith, used partnership funds to purchase a large tract of land, taking the title in his own name. A dispute arose between Brown and Smith, and Brown refused to recognize the land as partnership property on the ground that the legal title was vested in him because his name appeared in the conveyance. What are the rights, if any, of Smith?

_____

_____

_____

_____

_____

_____

_____

_____

_____

**CHAPTER 38
PARTNERSHIP:
RELATION TO
THIRD PERSONS**

Chapter 38 discusses (1) the classification of the authority of the partners, (2) the extent of the authority, (3) the liabilities of the partners for contractual obligations, torts, and crimes, (4) the effect of subsequent ratification of unauthorized acts of partners, (5) the duties and liabilities appertaining to the partnership that are created by estoppel, and (6) when admissions and representations made by a partner may be used as evidence against the partnership.

Fill-in Questions. Write the correct word or words in the blank spaces to complete the following statements.

1. An act of a partner, in order to bind another partner or the partnership, must be committed within the _____.
2. Express authority is _____ and _____ delegated to the agent orally or in writing.
3. _____ authority means that the principal is deemed to have delegated authority to the agent to act in conformity with the general customs of the business.
4. _____ or _____ made by any partner concerning partnership affairs within the scope of his authority is evidence against the partnership.
5. The courts agree that the relation of partners is founded on the doctrine of _____.

True-False Questions. Indicate whether each of the following statements is true or false by circling the T or F.

T   *F*   1. A partnership may be created by estoppel.
T   *F*   2. A partnership may be bound by ratification, estoppel, and admissions.
T   *F*   3. A partner does not have the implied authority to confess a judgment.
T   *F*   4. A partner does not have an insurable interest in the life of his copartners.
T   *F*   5. The implied authority to sell property is limited to property acquired for sale.

T   *F*   6. A partner will not be impliedly authorized to perform acts
                    which are not reasonably necessary, essential, usual, and
                    proper for carrying out the express authority.
T   *F*   7. The rights, duties, and functions of partners embody those
                    of agents.

Problems. *Analyze each of the following factual situations and state your
decision and the reason for your decision in the space provided.*

1. Clark, Lewis, and Dale were the members of a partnership engaged
    in the business of carrying on a clothing shop for men. Clark applied
    for and received a policy of fire insurance covering the inventory of
    the partnership. Clark individually paid the premiums, and he was
    named the beneficiary in the policy. In case the inventory of the
    partnership is destroyed by fire, should the proceeds of the insurance
    policy be paid to Clark or to the partnership?

_____

_____

_____

_____

_____

_____

_____

2. Brown, a nonacting partner, and Jones, the acting partner, were en-
    gaged in the illegal business of counterfeiting and selling federal
    reserve notes. The two were apprehended, and Brown proved that he
    did not participate in the counterfeiting of the notes nor in the selling
    of the notes. Should Brown be held liable?

_____

_____

_____

_____

_____

_____

3. Morris and Martin were the members of a partnership engaged in the building construction business. Morris sold two trucks that were used in the partnership to Dell, also a building contractor, for $5,000. Was the sale by Morris within the scope of the partnership business?

_____

_____

_____

_____

_____

_____

_____

_____

_____

_____

_____

4. Burke and Hill formed a partnership for the purpose of buying and selling real estate. They agreed that the title to all real property should be taken in the name of Burke and that he should sign all deeds of conveyance. What are the disadvantages of this agreement from the viewpoint of Hill?

_____

_____

_____

_____

_____

_____

_____

_____

_____

_____

5. List the acts expressly enumerated by the Uniform Partnership Act which, unless authorization has been given by the other partners or unless they have abandoned the business, require the unanimous consent by all the partners.

_____

_____

_____

_____

_____

_____

_____

_____

_____

_____

CHAPTER 39
PARTNERS:
RELATION TO
ONE ANOTHER

Chapter 39 explains the rules pertaining to the follow-ing: (1) the duty of each partner to account as a fidu-ciary and to render true and full information of all things affecting the partnership to the other partners; (2) the right of each partner (a) to inspect the partner-ship books, (b) to sue the partnership, (c) to receive a formal accounting, (d) to obtain compensation for ser-vices, (e) to receive indemnity and contribution, (f) to obtain interest on loans made to the partnership, (g) to share in the profits, (h) to share in the specific part-nership property, (i) to his interest in the partnership, and (j) to participate in the management of the part-nership.

Fill-in Questions. *Write the correct word or words in the blank spaces to complete the following statements.*

1. A partner who pays more than his share of the partnership obligations is entitled to _____ from his copartners.
2. A distinction is made between _____ and _____ for the purpose of determining the right of a partner to draw interest.
3. The _____ doctrine means that the courts treat real property as if it were personal property for the purpose of liquidation.
4. A partner who, by his wrongful act or negligence, creates an unneces-sary loss to the partnership is under a duty to _____ the partnership.
5. The Partnership Act provides that a partner holds the _____ partnership property as a _____ in partner-ship.
6. A partner's _____ in the partnership is his share in the profits and surplus.
7. The court, by the use of a _____, will charge the interest of a debtor-partner with an unsatisfied judgment.
8. The duty to account as a fiduciary operates to prevent a partner from making a _____ profit.

True-False Questions. Indicate whether each of the following statements is true or false by circling the T or F.

T   F   1.   A partner does not have a right to inspect the books of the partnership.

T   F   2.   It is unnecessary for third persons who desire to give notice to the partnership to give such notice to all the partners.

T   F   3.   A formal accounting is a necessary incident to a dissolution of a partnership.

T   F   4.   A partner's right in the specific partnership property is subject to dower, curtesy, and allowances to widows, heirs, and next of kin.

T   F   5.   The separate creditors of an individual partner may not reach the specific partnership property.

T   F   6.   A surviving partner is entitled to reasonable compensation for his services in winding up the partnership affairs.

T   F   7.   The information gathered by a partner from the partnership books may be used for purposes other than partnership purposes.

T   F   8.   A partner may not assign his right in the specific partnership property unless all the other partners join in the assignment.

Problems. Analyze each of the following factual situations and state your decision and the reason for your decision in the space provided.

1.   A partnership of Clark, Hill, and Jones was carrying on the business of growing and selling citrus fruit. The partnership agreement provided that the profits would be divided at the close of the harvesting season. Clark, who was traveling on partnership business for long periods of time, asked for a formal accounting before the close of the season, but Hill and Jones refused. Do you think Clark is entitled to a formal accounting?

_____

_____

_____

_____

_____

_____

_____

_____

2. Brown, a partner in the partnership of Brown, Smith, and Jones, assigned his interest in the partnership to Wilcox. Wilcox contends that the assignment gives him all the rights of a partner. Do you agree with this contention?

_____

_____

_____

_____

_____

_____

_____

_____

_____

_____

_____

_____

3. Explain how the Uniform Partnership Act makes it possible for the surviving partner as a part of the process of winding up to dispose of the real property of the partnership without the heirs or devisees of the deceased partner joining in the conveyance.

_____

_____

_____

_____

_____

_____

_____

_____

_____

_____

4. Morris, a member of a partnership carrying on the business of purchasing, developing, and selling real property, learned that a college was to be located on some property which adjoined property owned by the partnership. Would Morris be justified in purchasing the interest of the other partners without disclosing this information?

_____

_____

_____

_____

_____

_____

_____

_____

5. The partnership of Brown, Jones, and Smith was in the retail business of buying and selling small electrical appliances. Brown was the manager of the office; Jones was purchasing agent; and Smith was in charge of sales. Brown contends that as manager of the office he is the manager of all the business of the partnership. Is Brown correct?

_____

_____

_____

_____

_____

_____

_____

_____

CHAPTER 40
PARTNERSHIP:
DISSOLUTION,
WINDING UP,
TERMINATION

Chapter 37 explained the nature, creation, and property of the partnership; Chapter 38 explained the relation of the partners to third persons; and Chapter 39 explained the relation of the partners to one another. This chapter completes the chapters on partnership and explains (1) how a partnership may be dissolved (a) without violation of the partnership agreement and (b) in contravention of the agreement; (2) the rights, duties, and liabilities of the partners who continue to carry on the partnership until termination; and (3) the (a) winding up of the partnership business, (b) the distribution of the assets, and (c) the requirement of each parnter to share in the losses when the partnership is insolvent.

Fill-in Questions. *Write the correct word or words in the blank spaces to complete the following statements.*

1. In the winding-up process of the life of the partnership, the doctrine of _____ _____ is applicable where the individual partners, as well as the partnership, are insolvent.
2. The process of _____ brings the life of the partnership to an end.
3. The term _____ designates the time when the partners cease to carry on business together.
4. The partnership may be dissolved without violating the partnership agreement when the partnership is one _____.
5. Any change in the membership of a partnership produces, technically, the _____ of the existing partnership and the formation of a new one.
6. _____ automatically takes place when the winding up is completed and is the end of the life of the partnership.
7. The court may, in its discretion, appoint a _____ to wind up the partnership affairs where it is shown to be in the best interests of all persons concerned.

True-False Questions. Indicate whether each of the following statements is true or false by circling the T or F.

T F 1. A partnership may be dissolved without violating the partnership agreement by mutual agreement of all the partners.

T F 2. A partner may apply for a dissolution of the partnership because of insanity, incapacity, or misconduct of another partner.

T F 3. Temporary insanity and past insanity from which there has been a recovery is a proper ground for a judicial dissolution of a partnership.

T F 4. A partnership is dissolved by operation of law by any event which makes it unlawful for the members to carry on the business together.

T F 5. Sickness of a partner is not one of the risks incidental to a partnership relation.

T F 6. A partner may not apply for a dissolution of the partnership because of willful or persistent breach of the partnership agreement by another partner.

T F 7. The remaining partners may recover damages from a partner who dissolves a partnership in contravention of the partnership agreement.

T F 8. Failure of the partnership business will automatically terminate a partnership.

T F 9. The adjudication of bankruptcy of any partner, or of the partnership, operates to dissolve the partnership.

Problems. Analyze each of the following factual situations and state your decision and the reason for your decision in the space provided.

1. Brown and three others were the members of a partnership carrying on business under the partnership name of "Brown's." The partnership was formed on January 1, 1970, and was to exist for a period of five years. Brown became dissatisfied, and dissolved the partnership on June 1, 1970. Brown contends that the remaining partners must change the name of the partnership. Do you agree with this contention?

_____

_____

_____

_____

_____

_____

2. Morris, a member of the partnership of Morris, Martin, and Wilcox, retired from the partnership. Morris assigned his right in the partnership to Martin and Wilcox, who continued the business of the partnership. The three members did not, however, enter into an agreement with respect to the partnership debts. The old set of creditors of Morris, Martin, and Wilcox and the new set of creditors of Martin and Wilcox each claims a priority in the assets of the partnership. Which set of creditors is correct?

_____

_____

_____

_____

_____

3. Brown withdrew from the partnership of Brown, Smith & Jones. Smith, although he knew that Brown had withdrawn, entered into a contract in behalf of the partnership. Jones, who did not know that Brown had withdrawn, likewise entered into a contract in behalf of the partnership. Brown contends that under the Uniform Partnership Act he is not liable on either of these contracts. Decide.

_____

_____

_____

_____

_____

_____

_____

_____

_____

4. The partnership of Aaron and Adams was dissolved by the bankruptcy of Adams. Who has the right to wind up the partnership affairs?

_____

_____

_____

_____

_____

_____

5. The partnership of Linder, Lyle, and Lawson became insolvent. Each partner contributed $5,000 capital, the partnership owes $15,000 to creditors, and there are no assets in the partnership to pay the creditors. What is the individual liability of the partners?

_____

_____

_____

_____

_____

_____

6. When may a purchaser of a partner's interest apply for a dissolution of the partnership?

_____

_____

_____

_____

_____

_____

_____

CHAPTER 41
LIMITED PARTNERSHIP

The purpose of Chapter 41 is to explain some of the rules pertaining to a limited partnership, which is a modified form of partnership. This chapter is devoted to the rules pertaining to (1) the formation of a limited partnership, (2) the rights and liabilities of a general and limited partnership, and (3) the distribution of assets upon dissolution of the partnership.

Fill-in Questions. *Write the correct word or words in the blank spaces to complete the following statements.*

1. The Limited Partnership Act disallows the use of a _____ of a limited partner in the partnership name.
2. After dissolution of a limited partnership, general _____ are entitled to first distribution and _____ partners take priority over _____ partners.
3. A limited partner may not make his capital contribution in _____.
4. It has been held that a limited partner is entitled to a dissolution of the partnership when the _____ is carried on at a loss.

True-False Questions. *Indicate whether each of the following statements is true or false by circling the T or F.*

T   F   1. Limited partners are personally liable to the creditors of the partnership.
T   F   2. A general partner has all the rights and is subject to all the restrictions and liabilities of a partner in a partnership without limited partners.
T   F   3. A limited partnership may be created by an oral agreement.
T   F   4. A limited partnership may always carry on any business which could be carried on by a general partnership.

CHAPTER 42
CORPORATIONS:
INTRODUCTION;
PROMOTERS

Chapter 42, after introducing the student to the law of corporations and explaining the relation between the corporation and the state of its incorporation, discusses (1) the various kinds of corporations, (2) the function of the promoters of the corporation, (3) the expenses in promoting the corporation, (4) the statutory formalities prescribed by statute for the formation of the corporation, and (5) whether the corporation or the promoter is liable for the contracts entered into by the promoter prior to incorporation.

Fill-in Questions. *Write the correct word or words in the blank spaces to complete the following statements.*

1. The _____ theory conceives a corporation as being a legal entity, separate and distinct from its shareholders.
2. A _____ corporation is a corporation whose shares are held by a few shareholders or by a single individual.
3. A _____ granted by the state to the corporation is a contract between the state and the corporation.
4. Corporations are generally classified, with respect to the extent to which the incorporation statutes have been complied with, as corporation _____ and corporations _____.
5. Corporations are classified with respect to the state of their incorporation as _____ and _____.
6. The persons who sign the certificate of incorporation are known as the _____.
7. The promoter may not make a _____ profit.
8. The majority of the courts today apply the _____ of the contract theory in holding a corporation liable for breach of the promoter's contracts.

True-False Questions. *Indicate whether each of the following statements is true or false by circling the T or F.*

T   F   1.   All corporations today are chartered by a special legislative act.

T	*F*	2.

T *F* 2. Several states have authorized the learned professions to incorporate as professional service corporations.

T *F* 3. A corporation, for purposes of jurisdiction, is a citizen of any state by which it has been incorporated and the state where it has its principal place of business.

T *F* 4. The relation between the corporation and the state begins with the promotion of the corporation and continues until the corporation is terminated.

T *F* 5. Government, or public, corporations are created for private purposes.

T *F* 6. There is no distinction between a close corporation and a public issue corporation.

T *F* 7. Some state statutes expressly provide that the corporation when it comes into existence shall be liable for the necessary expenses of the promotion of the corporation.

T *F* 8. Innocent shareholders and creditors who have been defrauded by the promoter can assert a direct action against the promoter.

T *F* 9. The duties and liabilities of promoters are governed by the statutes of the various states.

T *F* 10. The typical certificate of incorporation is very brief.

T *F* 11. All of the states have enacted statutes requiring the certificate of incorporation to be filed in the county in which the principal place of business of the corporation is to be located.

T *F* 12. The organization of the corporation can ordinarily be accomplished by holding two meetings.

Problems. *Analyze each of the following factual situations and state your decision and the reason for your decision in the space provided.*

1. Brown, Jones, and three others owned all the shares of stock in the XYZ Corporation. Brown lent $10,000 to the corporation, which sum the corporation was unable to repay at the time repayment should have been made. Brown thereupon brought an action against Jones and the three other shareholders to recover the $10,000. Will he succeed?

_____

_____

_____

_____

_____

_____

_____

_____

2. A corporation was organized for charitable purposes. One of the shareholders contends that the corporation cannot hold title to real property because the corporation was not organized for the purpose of making a profit. Decide.

_____

_____

_____

_____

_____

_____

_____

_____

_____

_____

_____

3. The members of The Tennis Club organized a nonprofit unincorporated association. They purchased five acres of land and built a clubhouse and several tennis courts. Should the title to the land be held in the name of "The Tennis Club"?

_____

_____

_____

_____

_____

_____

4. A corporation organized under the laws of Colorado was prohibited from doing business in Oregon until it paid a fee of $250. The corporation contended that the requirement violated Article 4, Section 2, of

the United States Constitution, which provides: "The citizens of each state shall be entitled to all privileges and immunities of citizens in the several states." Do you agree with this contention?

_____

_____

_____

_____

_____

_____

_____

5. What is the distinction between a domestic and a foreign corporation?

_____

_____

_____

_____

_____

6. What functions are performed by the board of directors at its first formal meeting?

_____

_____

_____

_____

_____

_____

_____

_____

7. Explain the function of the promoter of a corporation.

_____

_____

_____

_____

_____

_____

_____

_____

_____

_____

7. Explain the function of the promoter of a corporation.

CHAPTER 43
CORPORATIONS:
CORPORATE
FINANCIAL
STRUCTURE

Chapter 43 is devoted to the manner in which a corporation is financed by the use of shares of stock and bonds. The rules of law pertaining to the following are explained: (1) how the corporation is financed by the use of bonds and shares of stock, (2) preincorporation and postincorporation subscriptions, (3) the various kinds of shares of stock, and (4) the methods of marketing the shares to the public.

Fill-in Questions. *Write the correct word or words in the blank spaces to complete the following statements.*

1. The issuance and sale of bonds are known as _____ or _____ financing.
2. The par value of _____ is stated upon the face of the certificate.
3. A _____ dividend means that if the preferred dividend is not paid in a given year, the dividend is not necessarily lost.
4. When the owners of the preferred shares of stock participate with another class of stock beyond the stipulated dividend, the shares are said to be _____ shares.
5. The issuance and sale of shares of stock are known as _____ or _____ financing.
6. _____ shares merely represent the proportionate interests of the shareholder in the total assets of the corporation.
7. Passed dividends are lost if the shares are _____.
8. Shares of stock which have been issued as fully paid when the subscriber has neither paid nor agreed to pay their full value are known as _____.
9. A share _____ is an option to purchase shares.
10. A share _____ is a dividing of the outstanding shares into a greater number of shares.
11. The usual _____ requires the corporation to redeem its shares at a fixed date.

T   *F*   1. A usual type of corporate bond is a written promise to pay a specified sum of money at a specified date with interest at a specified rate.

T   *F*   2. Preincorporation subscriptions are entered into for benefit of the shareholders.

T   *F*   3. Voting and nonvoting shares of stock give the owner of the shares either a right to vote or denies him such right.

T   *F*   4. Share warrants are frequently attached to bonds of preferred shares as an additional attraction to prospective purchasers.

T   *F*   5. Preferred shareholders are always given voting privileges.

T   *F*   6. The most common method of financing the beginning corporation is through the sale of share warrants.

T   *F*   7. A creditor cannot recover against a holder of watered stock until he has actually been injured.

Problems. Analyze each of the following factual situations and state your decision and the reason for your decision in the space provided.

1. Wilcox and a number of other persons entered into an agreement to form a corporation and to subscribe to its authorized capital stock. Wilcox thereafter decided to withdraw his subscription. Is Wilcox bound by the agreement, or may he withdraw his subscription?

_____

_____

_____

_____

_____

_____

_____

_____

2. Brown subscribed for 200 shares of stock in the XYZ Corporation. He agreed to pay for the shares in monthly installments, and the corporation agreed to issue the shares when the purchase price had been paid in full. Brown had paid a part of the purchase price, and the corporation was adjudicated a bankrupt. In those states which follow

the purchase-and-sale view, would Brown be obligated to pay the unpaid balance as against the claim of creditors?

_____

_____

_____

_____

_____

_____

_____

3. In problem 2 above, what would your answer be in those states which refuse to recognize the purchase-and-sale view?

_____

_____

_____

_____

_____

4. Jones is the holder of 500 shares of 5 percent preferred stock in the XYZ Corporation. The corporation earned profits so that it could have paid 10 percent annually on its outstanding shares of stock for two successive years, but during this time no dividends were declared. At the end of the third year the directors declared a dividend on the preferred shares. Does Jones have a right to receive dividends for the two years prior to the year in which the dividend was declared?

_____

_____

_____

_____

_____

_____

_____

_____

5. Jones owned 200 participating-preferred shares of stock in the XYZ Corporation. He received the regular 5 percent dividend, and the common shareholders also received a 5 percent dividend. There was remaining a surplus for additional dividends. How should this surplus be distributed?

_____

_____

_____

_____

_____

_____

_____

6. With respect to watered stock, what is the distinction between the "true-value" rule and the "good faith" rule?

_____

_____

_____

_____

_____

_____

_____

_____

CHAPTER 44
CORPORATIONS:
POWERS

The chief purpose of Chapter 44 is to explain the powers of the corporation. This chapter, however, also explains the liability of the corporation for torts and crimes. More specifically, this chapter explains the rules pertaining to (1) the inherent, express, and implied powers; (2) some particular powers of the corporation, such as the powers to make corporate gifts; and (3) the disregarding of the corporate entity and the doctrine of ultra vires as a limitation on the corporate powers.

Fill-in Questions. *Write the correct word or words in the blank spaces to complete the following statements.*

1. The _____, or incidental, powers of a corporation are those which are necessary to corporate existence.
2. Shares of stock which have been reacquired by the corporation that issued them are commonly referred to as _____ shares.
3. Nonrecognition of separate corporate existence is expressed in terms of "disregarding the corporate entity" or _____.
4. Transactions which are beyond the powers of the corporation are said to be _____.
5. The _____ powers of a corporation are ascertained by reference to the articles of incorporation and the statutes of the state under which the corporation was organized.
6. Transactions which are within the powers of the corporation are said to be _____.

True-False Questions. *Indicate whether each of the following statements is true or false by circling the T or F.*

T   *F*   1. A shareholder may prevent an anticipated ultra vires act by seeking an injunction in a court of equity.
T   *F*   2. An ultra vires contract is illegal.
T   *F*   3. Holding companies may not be formed for the purpose of creating a monopoly.
T   *F*   4. The implied powers of a corporation are those which are

necessary for the purpose of carrying out its express powers and the object of its incorporation.

T   **F**   5. An ultra vires contract which interferes with the rights of creditors is voidable at the suit of creditors.

T   **F**   6. Disregarding the corporate entity is limited in its scope to parent and subsidiary corporations.

T   **F**   7. A corporation has no implied power to make corporate gifts.

T   **F**   8. A corporation is prohibited from acting as a guarantor in all of the states.

Problems. Analyze each of the following factual situations and state your decision and the reason for your decision in the space provided.

1. The Electric Company, a corporation, was chartered to sell electricity to consumers in a large city. Do you think the company would have the implied power to buy and sell electrical appliances?

_____

_____

_____

_____

_____

_____

_____

_____

_____

2. It was the custom of The Supper Club, a corporation, to sell beer to minors in violation of a state statute. The penalty imposed by the statute was $5,000. Could The Supper Club successfully defend an action for violation of the statute with the defense of ultra vires?

_____

_____

_____

_____

_____

_____

_____

3. Brown and the XYZ Corporation entered into a contract whereby Brown agreed to purchase and the corporation agreed to sell certain machinery. Selling the machinery, however, was beyond the powers of the corporation. Would Brown be successful in an action to compel the corporation to deliver the machinery?

_____

_____

_____

_____

_____

_____

_____

_____

_____

_____

4. What is the general effect of the statutes that have been enacted which contribute to the decline of ultra vires as a defense?

_____

_____

_____

_____

_____

_____

_____

_____

_____

_____

_____

5. The incorporators of The Cabinet Corporation were the directors of The Lumber Corporation, which corporation by agreement was always to own at least 51 percent of The Cabinet Corporation. A shareholder of The Lumber Corporation contended that one corporation may not organize and subscribe to the original shares of stock of another corporation. Do you agree with this contention?

_____

_____

_____

_____

_____

_____

_____

_____

CHAPTER 45
CORPORATIONS:
RELATION TO
DIRECTORS
AND OFFICERS

*Chapter 45 is concerned primarily with the relation-
ship between the corporation and its directors and
officers. This chapter, however, deals not only with
this relationship but also with dividends. The rules explained pertain to (1) the qualifications, the compensation, the management function, and the meetings of
directors; (2) the fiduciary relationship occupied by
the directors; (3) the standard of care required of
directors; (4) the rights, duties, and liabilities of directors in declaring a dividend; and (5) the authority of
the different officers.*

Fill-in Questions. *Write the correct word or words in the blank spaces to
complete the following statements.*

1. The Securities Exchange Act of 1934 contains a provision designed to
   protect _____ shareholders against specula-
   tion by _____ with advance information.
2. _____ pertains to two or more corporations
   having directors in common.
3. A _____, or stock dividend, is said to be a
   dividend payable in shares of stock of the corporation.
4. A note which promises to pay a scrip dividend is known as a
   _____.
5. A director who is personally interested in a matter that is being considered by the board of directors is known as an _____.
6. A distribution to the shareholders in the form of notes or promises to
   pay the amount of the dividend at a certain future time is known as a
   _____ dividend.

True-False Questions. *Indicate whether each of the following statements is
true or false by circling the T or F.*

T   F   1.   The general manager of the corporation is the custodian of
                   the funds of the corporation and its disbursing officer.

189

T	*F*	2.	The officers of a corporation are agents of the corporation.
T	*F*	3.	The president of a corporation is the officer who keeps the minutes of the meeting of the shareholders and directors.
T	*F*	4.	The declaration of a cash, or property, dividend creates a debt from the corporation to the shareholder.
T	*F*	5.	Whether or not dividends shall be declared is left to the sound discretion of the shareholders.
T	*F*	6.	The vice-president of a corporation has authority by virtue of his office alone to enter into contracts in behalf of the corporation.
T	*F*	7.	A dividend is properly declared by a formal resolution of board of directors.
T	*F*	8.	All of the states, by statutory provision, impose a personal liability upon directors for the wrongful declaration and payment of dividends.
T	*F*	9.	The declaration of a share dividend involves the issuance of new shares to be distributed pro rata to the shareholders.
T	*F*	10.	A dividend payable in shares of stock of another corporation is called a property dividend.
T	*F*	11.	All of the states have enacted statutes which require a director to be a shareholder.
T	*F*	12.	The directors of a corporation occupy a fiduciary relationship to the corporation.

Problems. *Analyze each of the following factual situations and state your decision and the reason for your decision in the space provided.*

1. The Board of Directors of the XYZ Corporation declared a dividend at a time when the corporation had not paid or provided for the payment of the corporate debts. Was this a lawfully declared dividend?

_____

_____

_____

_____

_____

_____

2. A resolution of the XYZ Corporation provided that all checks were to be signed by the treasurer and countersigned by a director. The treasurer, by means of a series of ingenious excuses, obtained the countersignatures of certain of the directors to checks payable to cash.

He misappropriated the proceeds of the checks to his own use. May
the directors be required to make good the amounts so appropriated?

_____
_____
_____
_____
_____

3. What information should be specified in a resolution declaring a
    dividend?

_____
_____
_____
_____
_____
_____
_____
_____

4. It is a general rule that the board of directors does not have authority
    to make fundamental changes in the corporate organization without
    the consent of the shareholders. Enumerate some acts that generally
    fall within this rule.

_____
_____
_____
_____
_____
_____
_____

5. What is meant by a "scrip dividend," and when do the directors generally declare such a dividend?

_____

_____

_____

_____

_____

_____

_____

_____

_____

6. Explain when unlawful dividends which have been paid to shareholders are recoverable from the shareholders.

_____

_____

_____

_____

_____

_____

_____

CHAPTER 46
CORPORATIONS:
RELATION TO
SHAREHOLDERS

The last chapter explained the relationship between the directors and the corporation, and Chapter 46 explains the relationship between the shareholders and the corporation. This chapter, however, also explains the rules pertaining to investment securities. You should learn the rules pertaining to (1) the rights and liabilities of the shareholder, (2) the function of a proxy and voting trust as corporate control devices, (3) how the minority shareholders are enabled to secure representation on the board of directors by cumulative voting, (4) the pre-emptive right of shareholders to purchase newly authorized issues of shares, (5) the right to inspect the corporate books for a proper purpose, (6) the three general categories of suits by shareholders, (7) the meetings of shareholders, and (8) the issuance, transfer, and registration of shares of stock.

Fill-in Questions. *Write the correct word or words in the blank spaces to complete the following statements.*

1. The _____ form of agency, unless coupled with an interest, is revocable.
2. The holder of a voting trust has only the rights given him by his _____.
3. The aim of _____ voting is to enable minority shareholders to secure representation on the board of directors.
4. The Code defines a _____ of a security as a purchaser for value in good faith and without notice of any adverse claim.
5. The common-law _____ of a shareholder is his right to purchase a pro rata share of newly issued shares before the shares are offered to others.
6. The word _____ as used in the Code includes a person whose name is placed on a security to evidence that it represents a share in an enterprise.
7. The principal duty of the _____ is to guard against the issuance of shares in excess of the authorized capital stock and to countersign the certificate.

T   F   1. The provision of the Statute of Frauds pertaining to investment securities applies to any contract for the sale of securities irrespective of the amount involved.

T   F   2. The Code provides that a person who guarantees a signature of an indorser of a security warrants to the issuer that the signature is genuine, the signer was the appropriate person to indorse, and the signer had the legal capacity to sign.

T   F   3. The owner may not reclaim a stolen certificate transferred by a forged indorsement while it is still in the hands of a bona fide purchaser.

T   F   4. "Investment securities" covers only certificates of stock.

T   F   5. There is no distinction between a "call" and a "notice" of meetings of shareholders.

T   F   6. A representative suit is usually used to enjoin a threatened wrong by the corporation before it is consummated.

T   F   7. Cumulative voting permits each shareholder to multiply the number of votes to which he is entitled by the number of directors to be elected.

T   F   8. A proxy contest arises when there is a dispute between groups attempting to gain control or retain control of the board of directors.

T   F   9. An oral contract for the sale of investment securities is always enforceable.

Problems. *Analyze each of the following factual situations and state your decision and the reason for your decision in the space provided.*

1. Summarize the rights of a shareholder.

_____

_____

_____

_____

_____

_____

_____

2. Jones owed $5,000 to the Y Corporation on his subscription agreement. A creditor who had an unsatisfied judgment against the corpora-

tion brought a creditor's bill in equity against Jones to collect the $5,000. Decide.

_____

_____

_____

_____

_____

3. The bylaws of the XYZ Corporation provided that regular annual meetings of shareholders would be held at "1 P.M. on the first Monday in June each year in the main auditorium" of the corporation. Jones was not present at the regular meeting during which the shareholders elected a board of directors opposed by Jones. He contended that the election of the directors was not binding because notice of the meeting had not been given. Do you agree with this contention?

_____

_____

_____

_____

_____

4. The X Corporation proposed to merge with the Y Corporation. The shareholders, at a special meeting called for the purpose of voting on the proposed merger, voted in favor of the merger. The shareholders, as a part of the merger, voted in favor of authorizing the issuance of 20,000 shares of common stock. This new issue was to be issued to the Y Corporation in payment of 20,000 shares of stock in the Y Corporation. Are the shareholders entitled to exercise their pre-emptive right in the newly authorized issue of shares?

_____

_____

_____

_____

_____

5. A shareholder loaned the corporation $10,000. The corporation failed to repay the loan when it became due. May the shareholder sue the corporation in his individual capacity or must he bring a representative suit?

_____

_____

_____

_____

_____

_____

_____

6. Enumerate the warranties that are made by a selling shareholder to his purchaser.

_____

_____

_____

_____

_____

_____

_____

7. Enumerate the duties of the transfer agent when a certificate is presented for transfer.

_____

_____

_____

_____

_____

_____

_____

CHAPTER 47
CORPORATIONS:
TERMINATION

Chapter 47 concludes the chapters on corporations. This chapter is neither long nor difficult. The things you should learn are (1) the distinction between and the effect of consolidation and merger, (2) how a corporation may be dissolved by voluntary and involuntary dissolution, and (3) the qualified existence of a dissolved corporation.

Fill-in Questions. Write the correct word or words in the blank spaces to complete the following statements.

1. The assets of a _____ corporation belong to the shareholders.
2. In the _____ of corporations, two or more existing corporations are dissolved and a new single corporation is created.
3. The surviving corporation in a _____ absorbs the other corporations which are dissolved.
4. Dissolution of a corporation may be _____ or _____.

True-False Questions. Indicate whether each of the following statements is true or false by circling the T or F.

T   F   1. Neither consolidation nor merger involves the liquidation and winding up of the affairs of the corporation to the extent that the assets are distributed to the shareholders.

T   F   2. A corporation may not be granted perpetual existence.

T   F   3. Involuntary dissolution of a corporation may be brought about by a suit for dissolution of the corporation maintained by the shareholders.

T   F   4. If the liabilities of a dissolved corporation exceed the assets, a shareholder will be liable to creditors to the extent of the balance unpaid upon his shares.

SECURITIES REGULATION; ANTITRUST, LABOR RELATIONS 9

CHAPTER 48
SECURITIES REGULATION

The first part of Chapter 48 contains some definitions which are used exclusively in the law of securities. These definitions must be clearly understood before you proceed with your study of securities regulations. This chapter then (1) summarizes the securities and transactions that are exempted from the coverage of the Securities Act of 1933, (2) explains the procedure required by regulation C for preparing and filing a registration statement with the Securities and Exchange Commission and the action that may be taken prior to the effective date of the registration statement, (3) explains the procedure required by regulation A in order to take advantage of the exemption from regulation C, (4) explains the procedure required for registering and listing securities on a national securities exchange and the reporting requirements, (5) discusses the antifraud provisions of the Securities Act of 1933 and the Exchange Act of 1934, (6) explains the tests for determining what persons are considered to be beneficial owners and the reports that must be filed by such owners, (7) discusses the regulation of certain specified owners who are beneficial owners and the recapture of short-swing profits, (8) explains how corporate control contests are regulated, (9) enumerates the conditions that must be complied with in order to be classified as "persons deemed not to be underwriters," (10) briefly discusses the duties of the Securities and Exchange Commission, and (11) discusses the state securities statutes.

Fill-in Questions. *Write the correct word or words in the blank spaces to complete the following statements.*

1. Securities issued in small offerings where the aggregate offering price does not exceed _____ in a period of one year are exempted from the coverage of regulation C.

2. The term _____ means any _____, notice, circular, advertisement, letter, or communication which offers any security for sale or confirms the sale of any security.
3. An _____ transaction may be briefly defined as securities bought in one market and sold in another for purposes of profit arising in the differences in price in the two markets.
4. A means of acquiring control of a corporation, other than by winning a proxy contest, is through a device known as a _____ offer.
5. The state securities statutes are frequently referred to as the _____ laws.
6. The term _____ means any stock or similar security, or any security convertible into such a security, or any right to subscribe to purchase such a security.
7. The term _____ means securities acquired directly or indirectly from the issuer, or an affiliate of such issuer, in a transaction or chain of transactions not involving any public offering.
8. The term "issuer" as used in the definition of an underwriter, in addition to an issuer, includes an _____.
9. A cash tender offer is sometimes referred to as a _____ bid.
10. The two principal federal statutes relating to securities are the _____ Act and the Securities _____ Act.

True-False Questions. Indicate whether each of the following statements is true or false by circling the T or F.

T   *F*   1. The Securities Exchange Act relates primarily to the regulation of trading in securities.

T   *F*   2. The term "certified," when used in regard to financial statements, means certified by a notary public.

T   *F*   3. The Securities Act relates primarily to the issuance and distribution of securities.

T   *F*   4. The definition of the term "security" is limited in its scope to shares of stock and bonds.

T   *F*   5. Any security issued by building and loan associations is exempted from the coverage of the Securities Act.

T   *F*   6. Fractional undivided interests in oil or gas rights are exempted from the coverage of the Securities Act even though the aggregate offering price exceeds $250,000.

T   *F*   7. The exempted transaction which ordinarily permits investors to make casual sales of their securities is known as the private-placement exemption.

T   *F*   8. The provisions of the Securities Exchange Act regulating short-swing profits does not apply to beneficial owners of securities.

T   *F*   9.   In corporate control contests, the term "participant" includes any person or committee who solicits proxies.

T   *F*   10.   The Securities and Exchange Commission does not administer the Trust Indenture Act of 1939.

Problems. Analyze each of the following factual situations and state your decision and the reason for your decision in the space provided.

1.   The X Corporation issued securities in the amount of $400,000 during March 1974. The directors of the corporation conceded that it would be necessary to comply with the state blue sky laws, but contended that the corporation was completely exempted from the federal statutes regulating securities. Do you agree with this contention?

_____

_____

_____

_____

_____

_____

_____

2.   Brown, a dealer in securities, properly filed a registration statement with the Securities and Exchange Commission. Brown contended that the filing of the registration statement entitled him to transact business on the national exchanges. Do you agree with this contention?

_____

_____

_____

_____

_____

_____

_____

_____

3. Davis purchased 10 percent of a class of a registered equity security on April 1, 1974. Explain whether Davis would or would not be required to report this purchase to the Securities and Exchange Commission and to any national exchange.

_____

_____

_____

_____

_____

_____

_____

4. The X Corporation was incorporated on August 1, 1974, and filed a notification with the Securities and Exchange Commission on November 1, 1974. The corporation had not made a net income, and the amount of the offering made by the corporation was $40,000. Explain whether the corporation should or should not use an offering circular.

_____

_____

_____

_____

_____

_____

5. Explain the distinction between the three types of blue sky laws.

_____

_____

_____

_____

_____

_____

_____

CHAPTER 49
ANTITRUST: MONOPOLIES,
RESTRAINTS OF TRADE,
CONSPIRACIES

Chapter 49, after discussing the history of the anti-trust laws, (1) quotes the most important provisions of the Sherman Act; (2) explains the distinction between resale price maintenance contracts and price fixing; (3) uses the Klor's, Inc. v. Broadway-Hale Stores, Inc. case to illustrate the type of group boycott that is illegal; (4) enumerates the most often used remedies for violations of the Sherman Act; (5) after explaining the purpose of the Clayton Act, uses the International Salt Co. v. U.S. case to explain the type of business activity that is prohibited by tying sales and leases; (6) explains when exclusive-dealing contracts are considered to be illegal; (7) discusses the Celler-Kefauver Antimerger Act; (8) discusses the lawfulness and unlawfulness of discrimination in prices as provided by the Robinson-Patman Act; (9) briefly explains the duties of the Federal Trade Commission; and (10) explains when the state resale price maintenance contracts are valid.

Fill-in Questions. *Write the correct word or words in the blank spaces to complete the following statements.*

1. Resale _____ contracts are exempted from the coverage of the federal antitrust laws.
2. Price-fixing by joint activities between suppliers and distributors is known as _____ price-fixing.
3. Diversification could be the purpose of a _____ merger.
4. The Robinson-Patman Act is often referred to as the _____ Act.
5. A clause in a contract which binds retailers to the terms of a resale price maintenance contract irrespective of whether they did or did not enter into the contract is known as a _____ clause.
6. The first major antitrust law enacted by Congress was the _____ Act.

7. Acquisitions of _____, as well as stock, were prohibited by the Celler-Kefauver Act.

8. The purpose of the _____ laws is to permit fair trade pricing contracts for certain products for retail sale.

9. A _____ merger combines two businesses, one of which is a supplier-seller and the other a buyer-customer.

10. A _____ merger applies to acquisitions engaged in diverse and unrelated businesses, which businesses neither compete nor are related as buyer and customer.

True-False Questions. *Indicate whether each of the following statements is true or false by circling the T or F.*

T   *F*   1. Trade boycotts, or group boycotts, are not illegal under the antitrust laws.

T   *F*   2. The purpose of the Clayton Act was to supplement and strengthen the Sherman Act.

T   *F*   3. The rule pertaining to tying sales does not prevent a small company from attempting to break into the market in order to meet competition.

T   *F*   4. The antitrust laws provide that spendthrift trusts are illegal.

T   *F*   5. There is no distinction between resale price maintenance contracts and price-fixing.

T   *F*   6. The Robinson-Patman Act makes it illegal for a buyer to knowingly induce a discrimination in price.

T   *F*   7. The Federal Trade Commission Act gave the Federal Trade Commission investigative, legislative, and judicial powers.

T   *F*   8. All of the state constitutions have provisions prohibiting monopolies and combinations in restraint of trade.

T   *F*   9. Resale price maintenance contracts are valid in interstate commerce provided the law of the state where the resale is to be made permits this type of contract and the product bears a trade-mark, trade name, or trade brand.

T   *F*   10. Indirect methods of price discrimination are not illegal.

Problems. *Analyze each of the following factual situations and state your decision and the reason for your decision in the spaces provided.*

1. The A Corporation, the B Corporation, and the C Corporation entered into a contract fixing the price of glass windows in the City of Y. The effect of this contract was the elimination of competition in the City of Y. The Hardware Company, which was doing business in the City of Y, was thereby forced into bankruptcy. What remedy, if any, is available to the Hardware Company?

_____

_____

_____

_____

_____

_____

_____

2. A manufacturer furnished displays and demonstrations to all its customers who purchased supplies in the amount of $10,000 each month. The customers who purchased less than $10,000 contended that this practice was illegal; the manufacturer contended the practice was legal because competition had not been lessened. Decide.

_____

_____

_____

_____

_____

_____

3. Brown, who was engaged in the business of buying and selling small appliances, induced a distributor to sell appliances to him at a price lower than the price at which the distributor was selling to other customers in the same vicinity. The other customers contended that this was illegal. Do you agree with this contention?

_____

_____

_____

_____

_____

_____

_____

4. The X Corporation, which was engaged in the business of manufacturing certain farm machinery, acquired all of the assets of several competing corporations. The effect of this acquisition was to substantially lessen competition. Does this acquisition violate the antitrust laws?

_____

_____

_____

_____

_____

_____

5. Explain why the laws in this chapter are referred to as "antitrust" laws.

_____

_____

_____

_____

_____

_____

_____

CHAPTER 50
LABOR RELATIONS

Chapter 50, after briefly discussing the growth of the labor unions in the United States and the Railway Labor Act, (1) summarizes the labor practices defined by the Wagner Act to be unfair to employees; (2) explains how the Taft-Hartley Act left to the states the right to outlaw or restrict the closed shop and related union-security agreements; (3) enumerates certain labor practices by unions as unfair labor practices; (4) explains the eighty-day cooling-off period; (5) discusses the provisions of the Landrum-Griffin Act pertaining to the bill of rights for union members, the reporting requirements, and financial safeguards for labor organizations; (6) explains how the Civil Rights Act eliminates job discrimination; (7) discusses the Fair Labor Standards Act and enumerates the employees who are exempted from the provisions of the act; (8) explains the provisions of the Davis-Bacon Act, the Walsh-Healy Act, and the Federal Kickback Act as related to public works and contracts; (9) discusses the Occupational Safety and Health Act and the Social Security Act; (10) discusses the growth and purpose of unemployment compensation; (11) explains the state right-to-work laws; and (12) discusses the National Commission on State Workmen's Compensation Laws and enumerates the nineteen elements recommended by the Commission as essential to a modern workmen's compensation program.

Fill-in Questions. *Write the correct word or words in the blank spaces to complete the following statements.*

1. The word "labor" as used in the labor laws comprises _____ labor as well as manual labor.
2. It is an unfair labor practice for an employer to refuse to bargain _____ with the designated representative of the employees.
3. The requirement that an employer pay for work not performed is known as _____.

4. A clause in a contract of employment whereby the employee stipulates that he is not and will not become a member of a union is known as the _____ contract.

5. One of the most important agencies concerned with labor-management relations is the _____ Labor Relations Board.

6. A strike by employees against their own employer to gain their own objective is a _____ strike.

7. An agreement by an employer and a union that goods declared unfair by the labor organization will not be handled by the employer is known as a _____ agreement.

8. A term normally referring to state constitutional and statutory laws prohibiting the requirement of union membership as a condition of employment is _____ laws.

True-False Questions. Indicate whether each of the following statements is true or false by circling the T or F.

T F 1. The workmen's compensation laws provide a system of compensation for employees who are unemployed.

T F 2. The bill of rights for union members gives union members the right to vote on an increase of dues and fees.

T F 3. Labor organizations are required to adopt and file a copy of their constitution and bylaws with the Secretary of Labor.

T F 4. Embezzlement of union funds by those handling such funds was made a state crime by the Landrum-Griffin Act.

T F 5. One of the purposes of the Civil Rights Act is to eliminate job discrimination because of race, color, religion, sex, or national origin.

T F 6. The minimum-wage and overtime compensation provisions of the Fair Labor Standards Act apply to all employees, including bona fide executives.

T F 7. The Equal Pay Act of 1964 prohibits discrimination in wages against employees on the basis of race.

T F 8. The Social Security Act today covers only the employee when he or she retires.

T F 9. An employee covered by social security who becomes severely disabled before reaching the age of retirement is entitled to monthly disability benefits.

T F 10. The Federal Employment Tax Act imposes a tax equally on the employer and employee for the purpose of providing monthly checks to the employee when he or she becomes unemployed.

Problems. *Analyze each of the following factual situations and state your decision and the reason for your decision in the space provided.*

1. The union members of a national union were on strike, and the strike affected the national defense. Explain what action could be taken by the President of the United States.

    _____

    _____

    _____

    _____

    _____

    _____

    _____

    _____

    _____

    _____

2. Jones, a member of a national union, requested the union to give him a copy of the collective-bargaining agreement that he was working under. Is the union required to comply with this request?

    _____

    _____

    _____

    _____

    _____

    _____

    _____

    _____

    _____

    _____

3. Mary was employed by the X Corporation, and her job involved tailoring women's apparel to be shipped in commerce. The manager of the X Corporation contended that Mary was not subject to the

wage and hour provisions of the Fair Labor Standards Act because she was not employed in commerce. Do you agree with this contention?

_____

_____

_____

_____

_____

_____

_____

_____

4. What is the purpose of the Occupational Safety and Health Act of 1970?

_____

_____

_____

_____

_____

_____

_____

_____

5. What is the definition of the term "employer" as defined by the Employment Security Amendments Act of 1970?

_____

_____

_____

_____

_____

_____

_____

_____

PROPERTY

10

**CHAPTER 51
INTRODUCTION
TO PROPERTY**

The student is introduced to the law of property in Chapter 51. It is important that you learn (1) the distinction between (a) real and personal property, (b) tangible and intangible property, (c) public and private property, and (d) the restrictions on the ownership of property; and (2) the distinction between the forms of ownership. These classes of property and types of estates will be referred to in the chapters that follow.

Fill-in Questions. *Write the correct word or words in the blank spaces to complete the following statements.*

1. Property which has a physical existence is _____ property.
2. The distinguishing characteristic of an _____ is that it can only be held by husband and wife.
3. A _____ is an estate of survivorship held by two or more persons jointly with equal rights to share in its enjoyment during their lives.
4. A most important restriction on absolute ownership of property is the power of _____.
5. Property which has no physical existence but is only a right to receive property is _____.

True-False Questions. *Indicate whether each of the following statements is true or false by circling the T or F.*

T   *F*   1. The community property system is a part of the common law.
T   *F*   2. A tenancy by the entirety is not endowed with the attribute of survivorship.
T   *F*   3. The entire property in a joint tenancy passes to the last survivor.

T   F   4.   The general requisites necessary to constitute a joint tenancy are a unity of interest, a unity of title, a unity of time, and a unity of possession.

T   F   5.   Personal property is land and those things firmly attached to the land.

Name _____ Date _____

CHAPTER 52
THE NATURE OF
PERSONAL PROPERTY

Chapter 52 explains the distinction between chattels real and chattels personal, and how personal property may be acquired by occupancy, finding lost or mislaid property, accession, confusion, gift, and creation. This chapter is relatively simple, although some students have difficulty with the rules pertaining to accession and confusion.

Fill-in Questions. *Write the correct word or words in the blank spaces to complete the following statements.*

1. A gift _____ is a gift among the living.
2. In accession by _____, the chattel of one person who is the owner of a smaller unit is joined to the chattel of another person who is the owner of the larger unit.
3. Estates that endure for the life of the holder or longer are termed _____ estates.
4. _____ in possession include definite tangible and movable things.
5. A gift _____ is a gift in contemplation of death.
6. In accession by _____ a new chattel is created from the material of one person and the labor—sometimes labor and materials—of another.
7. Estates that endure for a term of years, or at the will of the parties, are termed _____ estates.
8. _____ in action include rights in property which can only be enforced by action.
9. _____, literally speaking, means that something has been added.

True-False Questions. *Indicate whether each of the following statements is true or false by circling the T or F.*

T   *F*   1. The common-law right to take wildlife is subject to control and regulation by the state.

T   *F*   2. Chattels personal in action are also called choses in action.

T   *F*   3. Confusion may only occur in connection with fungible goods.

T   *F*   4. In accession by adjunction, the title to the finished product generally passes to the owner of the principal chattel.

T   *F*   5. Chattels personal in possession are also called choses in possession.

T   *F*   6. The common-law right to acquire title by creation is not protected by statute.

T   *F*   7. Gifts of personal property may be gifts inter vivos, gifts causa mortis, and testamentary gifts.

Problems. Analyze each of the following factual situations and state your decision and the reason for your decision in the space provided.

1. Brown, who found a diamond ring, carried it to a jeweler for the purpose of having it appraised. The jeweler then learned that the ring was lost property. Does the jeweler or the finder have a better title to the ring?

_____

_____

_____

_____

_____

_____

_____

_____

2. An uncle delivered a horse to his nephew and stated that he was giving the horse as a Christmas gift. The nephew accepted the horse and thanked his uncle. The uncle learned that the nephew planned to enter the horse in a race and decided to revoke the gift. Does the uncle have the right to retake the horse?

_____

_____

_____

_____

3. Brown, who owned an automobile over forty years old, thought that the automobile was worthless. He thereupon towed the automobile to a nearby forest with no intention of ever retaking it. Jones found the automobile, and later sold it to Smith for $5,000 as a valuable antique. Brown contends that he is entitled to the $5,000. Do you agree with this contention?

4. Aaron wrongfully intermingled his olive oil with olive oil belonging to Adams. What facts must Aaron prove in order to reclaim his share of the oil?

_____

_____

_____

_____

_____

_____

_____

Brown, who owned an automobile and a ferry, worried, thought that the automobile was worth $3,800. He floated on board it towed it to a nearby junkyard. An old friend of Brown's salvaged it, took round the automobile, and he sold it to Smith for $5,000 was valuable salvage. Brown contends that he is entitled to the $5,000. Do you agree with this contention?

Interfering with interlining? Explain. If with valid telegram to pay Adams. What facts could Angle prove him/her to perform his share of the contract?

CHAPTER 53
THE NATURE OF
REAL PROPERTY

The rules explained in Chapter 53 are not difficult to understand, but this chapter is relatively long. The sections devoted to the two systems of land registration, abstracts, and title insurance are more descriptive than the remaining sections in this chapter. You should learn (1) to distinguish the various types of estates, as well as the various types of future interests; (2) how the title to land may be acquired, giving particular attention to adverse possession; (3) the rights which one person may have in the land of another person; (4) how a chattel affixed to real property will result in a fixture; and (5) why an owner of real estate should proceed cautiously in making payment to a building contractor because of the statutes giving a mechanic a lien on the real estate.

Fill-in Questions. *Write the correct word or words in the blank spaces to complete the following statements.*

1. The _____ is the deed commonly used to clear the title to real property.
2. _____ means an increase by the gradual deposit by water of solid material so as to cause land which was covered by water to become dry land.
3. A person who owns land on the bank of a stream or river is a _____ owner.
4. _____ is water beneath the surface of the earth not following a well-defined or known channel.
5. A sudden addition to land by the action of water, such as a flood, is known as _____.
6. _____ water is that which is diffused over the surface of the ground.
7. _____ is the support which land receives from the adjoining land.
8. An easement is _____ when it is created to benefit the possession of adjoining land.
9. A _____ is a nonpossessory interest in land.
10. An easement _____ is one which is not created to benefit the possessor of adjoining land.

11. The _____ is a system of land registration, but the system has met with little success in the United States.
12. The _____, or _____, is the highest interest one can possess in land.
13. The word "determinable" is used interchangeably with the words _____ or _____ to describe the fee simple determinable estate.
14. Life estates which come into existence by operation of law are known as _____ and _____.
15. An _____ is an estate which passes the title to the fee to some third person upon the happening of some event.
16. A _____ is a future estate left in the conveyor.
17. The most common method by which the title to real property may be acquired is by deed of conveyance, by the terms of which the owner of real property, known as the _____, conveys the title thereto to another person, known as the _____.

True-False Questions. Indicate whether each of the following statements is true or false by circling the T or F.

T   *F*   1. All of the statutes require the filing or recording of a claim of a mechanic's lien within a stated time in order to preserve the lien.

T   *F*   2. An unrecorded mechanic's lien can never have priority over any other recorded lien.

T   *F*   3. A chattel is, as a general rule, regarded as a fixture when it is so affixed as to be incapable of severance without material injury to the freehold.

T   *F*   4. A riparian owner may not take the water from the stream.

T   *F*   5. A chattel is regarded as a fixture when it is so necessary or convenient to the use of the realty that it is commonly accepted as a part of the realty.

T   *F*   6. A mechanic's lien may attach to any interest in real estate of a person at whose instance this improvement was made.

T   *F*   7. The doctrine of ancient lights is in force in all of the states.

T   *F*   8. A person may use all the surface water which gathers upon his land.

T   *F*   9. State statutes provide that percolating water is at the absolute disposal of the owner of the land.

T   *F*   10. A person who claims to be in possession of premises as a tenant cannot be said to be in hostile possession for the purpose of adverse possession.

T   *F*   11. Title to real property may not be transferred by judicial sale.

T   *F*   12.   Modern statutes have abolished the inchoate dower and curtesy of a wife and husband.

T   *F*   13.   Title insurance insures against loss through a defect in the title to real property and unknown and hidden hazards.

T   *F*   14.   There is no distinction between an abstract of title and the Torrens System of land registration.

T   *F*   15.   The recording statutes do not ordinarily make recording essential to the transfer of the title to real property as between the grantor and the grantee.

Problems. *Analyze each of the following factual situations and state your decision and the reason for your decision in the space provided.*

1. The tenant and the owner of a farm entered into a lease by the terms of which the tenant erected an icehouse upon the farm with the understanding that the tenant could remove the icehouse upon the expiration of the lease. Discuss whether or not the icehouse is personal property of the tenant which he can remove upon the expiration of the lease.

_____

_____

_____

_____

_____

_____

_____

_____

_____

_____

2. Brown, who was the owner of a fee-simple estate in Blackacre, died without leaving a will. Who is now the owner of Blackacre?

_____

_____

_____

_____

3. Jones granted and conveyed by warranty deed a certain tract of land adjoining a church to the church upon the condition that the land be used as a parking lot for the church. The church was thereafter moved to another location, and the land was no longer used by the church. (1) What type of estate did Jones convey to the church, and (2) does the church still own the land?

4. What interest would Brown have left in real property if he conveyed the property to his son for life, then to Smith for ninety-nine years?

5. Aaron conveyed a tract of land to Aaron, Jr., upon the condition that if Aaron, Jr., graduated from college the title to the land should vest in his daughter, Mary. (1) What type of estate did Aaron convey to Aaron, Jr., and (2) when will the land vest in Mary?

_____

_____

_____

_____

_____

_____

_____

_____

_____

_____

_____

6. What is the distinction between a remainder and an executory interest?

_____

_____

_____

_____

_____

_____

_____

_____

_____

_____

_____

_____

_____

7. What is the distinction between an appurtenant easement and an easement in gross?

_____

_____

_____

_____

_____

_____

_____

_____

8. A building contractor constructed a new house for Brown. Brown paid the contractor, but the contractor failed to pay Jones, a subcontractor. The subcontractor filed a mechanic's lien upon the new house. Will Brown be required to pay Jones?

_____

_____

_____

_____

_____

_____

_____

_____

_____

_____

CHAPTER 54
LANDLORD AND TENANT

Chapter 54, like many of the other chapters, is concerned with a familiar subject. You should understand (1) how the relation of landlord and tenant is created, (2) the distinction between the various classes of tenancies, (3) the duties and liabilities of the landlord and the tenant, (4) when a lease may be assigned and the effect of the assignment, (5) the effect of subleasing, (6) the methods whereby the relation of landlord and tenant may be terminated, and (7) how the various classes of tenancies are terminated at the expiration of the term.

Fill-in Questions. *Write the correct word or words in the blank spaces to complete the following statements.*

1. The expression _____ is applied to all tenancies less than a freehold for a fixed period.
2. The person who gives the possession and use of real property is known as the landlord or _____.
3. A _____ is a tenancy that will continue for another period equal to the one that has expired.
4. The person who is given the possession and use of real property is known as the tenant or _____.
5. A tenant at _____ is one who wrongfully continues in possession after coming into possession rightfully.
6. A tenancy which is held at the will of either the landlord or the tenant is known as a _____.
7. The destruction, misuse, or alteration of the premises by the tenant is known as _____.
8. The giving up of a lease by the tenant before the expiration of the term is known as _____.

True-False Questions. *Indicate whether each of the following statements is true or false by circling the T or F.*

T   *F*   1. Statutes in all of the states require that notice of the termination of a periodic tenancy must be in writing.

T   *F*   2. A lease may be terminated by "surrender" by mutual agreement or by operation of law.

T   *F*   3. A tenant is obligated to pay the rent even though he has been evicted by a person having a title paramount to that of the landlord.

T   *F*   4. The device used by the landlord for the collection of rent under modern statutes is known as distress.

T   *F*   5. In a few states, public health and safety laws provide that the premises must be kept in good repair by the owner.

T   *F*   6. A landlord who wrongfully disturbs or interferes with the possession or enjoyment of the premises by the tenant may constitute a constructive eviction of the tenant.

T   *F*   7. A tenant at sufferance has no election to regard himself as a tenant.

T   *F*   8. There is no distinction between a tenancy at will and a holding over under a tenancy for years.

T   *F*   9. In most of the states, leases for a period of more than one year—sometimes three years—must be in writing to be enforceable.

Problems. Analyze each of the following factual situations and state your decision and the reason for your decision in the space provided.

1. Barsh leased an apartment in a building, and a fire destroyed the building. The landlord contended that Barsh remained liable for the rent notwithstanding the destruction of the building. Do you agree with this contention?

_____

_____

_____

_____

_____

_____

2. The tenant and the landlord entered into a lease whereby the lease was to continue until all the pine trees had been cut and removed. The tenant contends that this provision created a tenancy for years. Do you agree with this contention?

_____

_____

_____

3. Brown, the tenant, and Jones, the landlord, entered into an agreement for the lease of a building. Brown was to have possession of the building on June 1, 1970. However, Brown could not take possession of the premises because the premises were occupied. What remedy, if any, is available to Brown?

4. How may a tenancy at will and a tenancy at sufferance be terminated?

5. Davis, who had leased a building from Jones for a period of ten years, subleased the building to various tenants with the consent of Jones. Many of the tenants failed to pay the rent as it became due, and Jones brought an action against the sublessees to collect the rent. Decide.

_____

_____

_____

_____

_____

_____

_____

_____

_____

6. The landlord and the tenant entered into a lease for a fixed term of twenty years. The tenant died, and the executor of his estate contended that the lease was thereby terminated. Under what circumstances would the executor be correct?

_____

_____

_____

_____

_____

CHAPTER 55
REAL ESTATE
MORTGAGES

The student will have noticed that Part 10, "Property," consists of a number of subjects. Chapter 55, like the last four chapters, does not contain difficult rules as did some of the chapters governed by the Uniform Commercial Code. You should, however, understand (1) the distinction between the title and the lien theory of mortgages, (2) the distinction between a deed of trust and an installment land contract, (3) the maxim "once a mortgage, always a mortgage," (4) the description given of the form of the mortgage, (5) the obligation for which the mortgage is given as security, (6) how the mortgagor and the mortgagee may transfer their respective interest in the mortgaged property, and (7) the different types of foreclosure.

Fill-in Questions. *Write the correct word or words in the blank spaces to complete the following statements.*

1. There are three parties to a deed of trust transaction: the _____, the _____, and the _____.
2. The _____ of real estate mortgage recognizes the mortgagor as the owner but gives the mortgagee a lien against the mortgaged property.
3. The creditor, or lender, is known as the _____.
4. The debtor—the person who borrows the money—is known as the _____.
5. The courts make a distinction between _____ and _____ advances.
6. Foreclosure by _____ is used in a majority of the states.

True-False Questions. *Indicate whether each of the following statements is true or false by circling the T or F.*

T *F* 1. The title theory of real estate mortgages prevails in most of the states today.
T *F* 2. The installment land contract is ordinarily drawn in favor of the vendor.

T   *F*   3. In most of the states, the mortgagee may not transfer his interest.

T   *F*   4. In practically all of the states, the mortgagor may redeem the mortgaged property after a judicial sale by paying to the purchaser the amount for which the property sold.

T   *F*   5. A provision in a mortgage reserving the power unto the mortgagee to sell the mortgaged property within a designated time after default by the mortgagor is recognized in a number of states.

T   *F*   6. Strict foreclosure of the mortgaged property is in wide use in the United States.

T   *F*   7. In a few states, the mortgagee is permitted to take possession of the mortgaged property upon default by the mortgagor in a foreclosure by entry and possession.

Problems. Analyze each of the following factual situations and state your decision and the reason for your decision in the space provided.

1. Baker, who owned a 140-acre farm, borrowed x thousands of dollars from Cabot. Baker executed a mortgage on the farm to secure the loan, and the mortgage contained an after-acquired property clause. A month later, Baker purchased another tract of land consisting of 80 acres. Baker thereafter, and prior to any knowledge by Cabot of the purchase, sold the 80 acres to Davis, who had no knowledge of the mortgage with the after-acquired property clause. What are the rights of Cabot and Davis with respect to the 80 acres?

_____

_____

_____

_____

_____

_____

_____

_____

_____

_____

_____

_____

2. Brown, the trustor, borrowed $30,000 from The Finance Company, the beneficiary. The conveyance securing the loan named Jones the trustee, and he held the legal title. Brown defaulted in his monthly payments, and Jones was then under a duty to foreclose the deed of trust. Explain the duties of Jones in making the sale.

_____

_____

_____

_____

_____

_____

_____

_____

_____

3. When does the vendee in an installment land contract acquire title to the land?

_____

_____

_____

_____

_____

_____

_____

_____

_____

_____

4. In a mortgage to secure future advances, the mortgagee made one advance, a junior lien attached, and the mortgagee was contemplating a further advance. Will the new advance have priority over the junior lien? Explain the two views in your answer.

_____

_____

_____

_____

_____

_____

_____

_____

_____

_____

_____

WILLS AND TRUSTS

11

CHAPTER 56
WILLS AND ESTATES
OF DECEDENTS

The purpose of Chapter 56 is to give the student a general survey of the law of wills and estates of decedents. The student who studies the chapter will understand the importance of making a will. You should learn (1) the minimum requisites necessary for the execution, modification, and revocation of the will; (2) that a holographic will, a nuncupative will, and soldiers' and sailors' wills are special types of wills; (3) how abatement and ademption will affect the property devised and bequeathed; (4) how a decedent's property will descend when the decedent dies intestate; and (5) the duties of a personal representative in administering the estate.

Fill-in Questions. *Write the correct word or words in the blank spaces to complete the following statements.*

1. The _____ most often fixed by statute is twenty-one years.

2. _____ occurs when changed circumstances render impossible the performance of a provision in a will.

3. _____ is the process of determining the distribution of assets left by a testator at his death when such assets are insufficient to satisfy the provisions of his will.

4. The term _____ means the executor, executrix, administrator, or administratrix.

5. Statutes frequently provide that administration of the estate of a decedent shall be under the supervision of the _____ court or the _____ court.

6. The person appointed by the court to administer the estate of a person who dies intestate is referred to as an _____ if such person is a man; if a female, she is referred to as an _____.

7. A person who dies leaving a will is said to die _____, and a person who dies without leaving a will is said to die _____.

8. The person designated by a testator in a will is referred to as the

_____ if the person is a male; if a female, she is referred to as an _____.

9. The instrument declaring the executor to be duly qualified to act as executor is known as _____.

10. A will written entirely in the handwriting of the executor is known as a _____.

11. An oral will made by the testator in his last illness is known as a _____.

12. Two common ways in which descendants inherit are known as _____ and _____.

True-False Questions. *Indicate whether each of the following statements is true or false by circling the T or F.*

T F 1. In all of the states, a will may only be revoked by a codicil.

T F 2. All of the states have enacted statutes setting forth specific requirements which must be complied with in order to revoke a will.

T F 3. The doctrine of revocation of a will by operation of law is recognized in all of the states.

T F 4. Soldiers' and sailors' wills may be oral or written, but they are ordinarily limited to personal property.

T F 5. Statutes decide the manner in which real and personal property of the decedent will be inherited when a person dies intestate.

T F 6. The administration of an estate may never be dispensed with.

T F 7. A surviving spouse is entitled to all the real property of the decedent even if there are surviving children.

Problems. *Analyze each of the following factual situations and state your decision and the reason for your decision in the space provided.*

1. Davis, who was in his last illness, asked three persons to act as witnesses to his oral will. He stated that it was his intention to leave all his property, real or personal, to a certain charitable organization. In a state that recognizes nuncupative wills, the heirs of Davis contend that the real property should descend to the heirs. Do you agree with this contention?

_____

_____

_____

_____

_____

_____

_____

_____

2. Explain how the executor may prove a will by witnesses.

_____

_____

_____

_____

_____

_____

_____

_____

_____

3. Enumerate the overall duties of the personal representative in the administration of an estate.

_____

_____

_____

_____

_____

_____

_____

_____

_____

_____

_____

4. Under the statutes of descent and distribution, who are the (a) surviving descendants, (b) surviving ascendants, and (c) surviving collaterals?

_____

_____

_____

_____

_____

_____

_____

_____

5. John Brown and Mary Brown, husband and wife, owned all their property as tenants by the entirety. After the death of John Brown, will it be necessary for Mary Brown to administer his estate?

_____

_____

_____

_____

_____

_____

6. What is the generally accepted formula for determining the mental capacity of a person to make a will?

_____

_____

_____

_____

_____

_____

_____

_____

CHAPTER 57
TRUSTS

The first part of Chapter 57 is concerned with an express trust, and the remainder of the chapter deals with the implied trusts and trust administration. You should understand (1) the minimum requirements necessary to create an express trust, giving particular attention to the Rule against Perpetuities and the Rule against Accumulations; (2) the distinction between a resulting trust and a constructive trust, (3) the powers and duties of the trustee; (4) the remedies available to the beneficiaries for mismanagement of the trust; and (5) how a trust is terminated.

Fill-in Questions. *Write the correct word or words in the blank spaces to complete the following statements.*

1. The subject matter of the trust, which is sometimes referred to as the trust property or the trust corpus, is known in legal parlance as the
    _____.

2. A trust will not result unless the _____, sometimes called the trustor, intends to create a trust.

3. A power peculiar to charitable trusts, and which is confined to charitable trusts only, is the _____ of a court of equity.

4. The purpose of the _____ is to limit the time during which a dead person may control property and to facilitate the marketability of property.

5. A trust created by the will of the settlor is known as a _____ trust.

6. A savings bank trust is sometimes referred to as the _____ trust, or a _____ trust.

7. A _____ trust is created when the purpose of the settlor is to protect a beneficiary who is incompetent, inexperienced, or immature.

8. A trust which has for its purpose the accomplishments or advantages to society is known as a _____ trust.

9. The two classes of implied trusts which are generally recognized are the _____ trust and the _____ trust.

10. A trust which arises independently of any actual or presumed intention of the parties is known as a _____ trust.

11. A _____ trust, sometimes referred to as a _____, or _____, or _____ trust, requires no action on the part of the trustee beyond turning over money or property to the beneficiary.
12. The doctrine of _____ allows the settlor to demand a return of the trust property when he is the sole beneficiary.

True-False Questions. Indicate whether each of the following statements is true or false by circling the T or F.

T   *F*   1.   The terms of a trust are frequently fixed to last during minority, until the marriage of a stated person, for life, for a period of years, or for some similar standard.
T   *F*   2.   A beneficiary may trace the trust fund into the hands of a bona fide purchaser who purchases the trust property in good faith and for value.
T   *F*   3.   A beneficiary may, when the trustee is preparing to commit a breach of trust, obtain an injunction against the wrongful act.
T   *F*   4.   A trust will not result from precatory expressions alone.
T   *F*   5.   A charitable trust which cannot be carried out in the precise manner prescribed by the donor will be transferred to another purpose that seems to be as near to the intention of the donor as existing conditions permit.
T   *F*   6.   Recent statutes exempt trusts for the establishment of pension funds or profit-sharing trusts by corporations for the benefit of their employees from the operation of the Rule against Perpetuities.
T   *F*   7.   All of the state statutes require the trust instrument to be in writing.
T   *F*   8.   A trust will fail if the trustee is given the discretion to select as the beneficiary the most worthy from a class.
T   *F*   9.   A constructive trust is said to include all those instances when any person acquires property under any circumstances which would make it unjust or inequitable for him to retain it.
T   *F*   10. In broad terms, the trustee has those implied powers which are reasonably necessary for him to carry out the purpose of the trust.
T   *F*   11. A trustee is permitted to purchase the trust property for himself or sell his own property to the trust.

Problems. Analyze each of the following factual situations and state your decision and the reason for your decision in the space provided.

1. Bates conveyed certain land to Cabot in trust for Tom, the son of

Bates. Cabot refused to accept the trust. What effect does this have on the rights of the son, Tom?

_____

_____

_____

_____

_____

_____

_____

_____

_____

_____

2. Cabot created a trust for the benefit of a charitable organization. Cabot thereafter changed his mind and decided he would prefer to create the trust for a certain private university. Could Cabot change the beneficiary without a provision in the trust agreement for modification or revocation of the trust?

_____

_____

_____

_____

_____

_____

_____

_____

_____

_____

3. Jones, in anticipation of financial difficulties, executed a spendthrift trust wherein he made himself the sole beneficiary and the sole trustee. Will the creditors of Jones succeed if they attack the validity of this trust?

_____

_____

_____

_____

_____

_____

_____

_____

_____

_____

_____

4. Brown, who was named the trustee in a trust agreement, accepted the trusteeship. He thereafter decided that the trusteeship was too time-consuming, and he submitted his resignation to the beneficiaries. Are the beneficiaries the persons to accept the resignation?

_____

_____

_____

_____

_____

_____

_____

_____

_____

_____

5. Davis, in anticipation of making profits by dealing in shares of stock, executed a trust and designated himself as trustee of all such profits for the benefit of his three children. At the time the trust was executed, he did not own any shares of stock. Is this a valid trust?

_____

_____

_____

_____

_____

_____

_____

_____

_____

_____

6. The College Club, a nonincorporated association, was named the trustee in a trust instrument. (a) What would prevent the association from qualifying as a trustee, and (b) does this mean that the trust will fail?

_____

_____

_____

_____

_____

_____

_____

_____

_____

_____

_____

7. Enumerate the trusts that are exempt from the Rule against Accumulations.

_____

_____

_____

_____

_____

_____

_____

_____

_____

INSURANCE, SURETYSHIP, GUARANTY, BANKRUPTCY 12

CHAPTER 58
THE INSURANCE CONTRACT

Chapter 58 is the first of two chapters concerned with insurance. These two chapters, however, do little more than present some of the fundamental principles of the law of insurance. You should understand (1) the most important and usual types of insurance and types of risks, and the most usual kinds of life and property insurance policies; (2) the distinction between agents and brokers; (3) the terminology used in the formation of the contract of insurance; (4) the representations and warranties ordinarily made by the applicant to the prospective insurer; (5) when policies of insurance may be assigned; (6) the insurer's right of subrogation; and (7) the duration and termination of the insurance contract.

Fill-in Questions. *Write the correct word or words in the blank spaces to complete the following statements.*

1. Ordinary life insurance is sometimes referred to as _____ or _____.

2. A _____ covers property without regard to its location at the time of the loss.

3. Warranties are _____ if they represent facts that exist at the time they are made.

4. Warranties are _____ if they represent that certain things must be complied with in the future.

5. A marine policy which uses the words _____ a stated port to another port attaches and becomes effective while the vessel is still in the harbor.

6. A _____ is an agent who has limited power to contract.

7. A binder is sometimes referred to as an _____; it is sometimes referred to as a _____; and it is sometimes referred to as a _____.

8. The willful misconduct of the master or crew which is prejudicial to the owner is known as _____.

9. The insurance company is the _____, and the person whose life or property is insured is known as the _____.

10. The intentional act of throwing goods overboard to lighten a vessel in danger of being lost or wrecked is known as _____.

True-False Questions. *Indicate whether each of the following statements is true or false by circling the T or F.*

T   *F*   1. In a policy of marine insurance, the insurer is not liable if there is a voluntary deviation from the agreed voyage.

T   *F*   2. The prepayment of premiums is always required as a condition to the validity of the contract in all types of insurance.

T   *F*   3. The stock company writes most of the fire and casualty insurance in the United States.

T   *F*   4. Statutes have been enacted in most of the states which completely abolish the common-law rules of warranty.

T   *F*   5. The courts generally hold that nonwaiver clauses have no effect in restricting the authority of a general agent who has full power to contract for insurance on behalf of the insurer during the time the contract is being entered into.

T   *F*   6. In the absence of some prohibition against assignment, a life insurance policy may be assigned without the consent of the insurer.

T   *F*   7. Nonforfeiture provisions are always included in a term policy.

T   *F*   8. Reinstatement clauses are rarely found in policies of life insurance.

T   *F*   9. Policies of insurance other than life frequently give the insurer the option to cancel the policy upon giving notice to the insured.

T   *F*   10. Liability insurance embraces all policies whereby the insurer assumes the risk of liability for damage to the person or property of a third person.

T   *F*   11. A broker is generally under employment from one particular insurance company.

T   *F*   12. A general agent has broad apparent authority.

Problems. *Analyze each of the following factual situations and state your decision and the reason for your decision in the space provided.*

1. Martin, an infant, insured his workshop against loss by fire. The workshop was destroyed by fire, but the insurance company refused to pay the proceeds of the policy to Martin on the ground that the policy

was not binding because of infancy. Would Martin recover in an action against the company to recover the proceeds?

_____

_____

_____

_____

_____

_____

2. Jones, who had been issued a policy of insurance on the life of his wife, had paid the premiums for over ten years at the time his wife died. The insurance company offered to return the premiums that Jones had paid but refused to pay the proceeds of the policy on the ground that Jones had no insurable interest in the life of his wife. Would Jones recover in an action against the company to recover the proceeds?

_____

_____

_____

_____

_____

3. Davis applied for and received fire insurance on a certain building. He failed, however, to disclose to the agent of the insurance company that a fire was raging in the vicinity of the property sought to be insured. The fire destroyed the building, and the insurance company claims that the contract of insurance is voidable. Decide.

_____

_____

_____

_____

_____

_____

_____

4. In an action to recover the proceeds of a policy of fire insurance, Brown, the insured, attempted to show by parol evidence that he told the insurance agent that the property insured was constructed of wood and that the agent answered in the application "constructed of brick." Under what circumstances would this evidence be excluded?

_____

_____

_____

_____

_____

_____

_____

5. A policy of insurance contained an "entire-contract" provision. How do the courts generally interpret this provision?

_____

_____

_____

_____

_____

_____

6. What is the chief distinction between representations and warranties?

_____

_____

_____

_____

_____

_____

_____

CHAPTER 59
STANDARD POLICIES AND PROVISIONS

The purpose of Chapter 59 is to explain some of the standard clauses that are contained in insurance policies. The organization of the chapter is relatively simple. The first sections explain the clauses contained in property insurance policies, and the remaining sections explain clauses contained in life insurance policies. You should understand these clauses and how they have been interpreted by the courts.

Fill-in Questions. *Write the correct word or words in the blank spaces to complete the following statements.*

1. The effect of the _____ clause is to place liability on each insurance company for its proportionate share of the loss when the property is insured by more than one company.

2. The theory of the _____ clause is based upon the reasoning that the beneficiary, after the premiums have been paid for a number of years, should not be met with a contest to determine whether the insurance ever had any validity.

3. The courts, in construing the _____ clause, make a distinction between "vacant" and "unoccupied."

4. The New York standard _____ clause insures the interest of the mortgagee as fully and to the same extent as if he had taken out a policy direct from the insurer.

5. The _____ statutes are ordinarily applicable only with respect to real property and only in case of total loss.

6. A _____ clause provides that if the insured fails to carry insurance equal to a stated percentage of the value of the property insured, the insured is a coinsurer for the uninsured excess.

7. A _____ is a small printed form containing a desired change in the policy.

True-False Questions. *Indicate whether each of the following statements is true or false by circling the T or F.*

T   *F*   1. Life and accident policies giving the insurer the right to make an autopsy in case of death are held to be invalid provisions by the courts.

T   *F*   2. Coinsurance is now prohibited in all of the states by statute.

T   *F*   3.   Both the mortgagor and the mortgagee have a separate and distinct insurable interest in the mortgaged property.

T   *F*   4.   Insurance policies commonly contain a clause to the effect that the insurer shall not be liable while the insured premises are vacant or unoccupied for a stated number of days.

T   *F*   5.   The 1943 standard policy direct-loss-by-fire clause covers every loss or damage to the insured property necessarily flowing from the occurrence of the fire or lightning.

T   *F*   6.   The insured is under a duty to mitigate the damage caused by fire by removing goods from the path of the fire whenever this is possible.

T   *F*   7.   The general effect of an increase-the-hazard clause is to place the burden on the insurer to prove that the breach increased the risk or contributed to the loss.

T   *F*   8.   Life policies ordinarily grant a grace period of two months during which the premiums may be paid.

T   *F*   9.   The usual form of good health clause provides that the policy shall not take effect unless the insured is in "good" or "sound" health when the policy is delivered.

T   *F*   10.   External and visible signs of injury are confined to injuries, such as broken bones and bruises.

Problems. Analyze each of the following factual situations and state your decision and the reason for your decision in the space provided.

1.   What is the purpose of the diminished liability clause?

_____

_____

_____

_____

_____

_____

_____

_____

_____

2.   The policy of insurance contained a provision that the insurer would not be liable for loss caused by explosion. The insured property was

practically destroyed by fire when an explosion occurred. What amount, if any, will the insured be able to recover?

_____

_____

_____

_____

_____

_____

_____

_____

_____

_____

3. What are the duties of the insured when the insurance policy contains an iron-safe clause?

_____

_____

_____

_____

_____

_____

_____

_____

_____

_____

4. Brown had insurance for $20,000 with the X Company for damage caused by fire. He also had a similar policy with the Y Company for $20,000. The insured building, which had a value of $20,000, was totally destroyed by fire. How much could Brown recover?

5. What are the duties required of the insured by the standard fire policy with regard to notice and proof of loss?

CHAPTER 60
NATURE OF
SURETYSHIP
AND GUARANTY

*The student who understood the section Promise to
Answer for the Debt of Another, which was explained
in Chapter 10, "Contracts Required to Be in Writing,"
should have little trouble in understanding the suretyship and guaranty contract. You should, however,
learn from a study of Chapter 60 (1) how the suretyship and guaranty contract is formed; (2) the distinction between the surety and indorser, the surety and
indemnitor, and the surety and guarantor; (3) the distinction between the general and special guaranty, the
temporary and continuing guaranty, and the absolute
and conditional guaranty; (4) the right of the creditor
against the debtor, the surety, and the security; and
(5) the various classes of surety bonds.*

Fill-in Questions. *Write the correct word or words in the blank spaces to
complete the following statements.*

1. Bonds which public officers are required by statute to give as a condition of entering upon the duties of the office are known as _____
bonds.
2. Three persons are involved in a suretyship contract: the _____,
or obligor, who becomes obligated to the _____,
or obligee, and the _____, who promises the
creditor to answer for the default of the debtor.
3. The person who contracts to save another person from some legal
consequence is known as the _____.
4. Surety bonds may be classified as _____ bonds
and _____ bonds.
5. A bond which is primarily for the performance of the work is known
as a _____ bond.
6. A bond which is primarily for the payment of laborers and materialmen is known as a _____ bond.
7. _____ bonds are ordinarily entered into by
companies to indemnify an employer.
8. The promise of the _____ is to perform if the
debtor cannot perform.

True-False Questions. *Indicate whether each of the following statements is true or false by circling the T or F.*

T   *F*   1. The purpose of requiring a litigant to furnish a judicial bond is to indemnify the adverse party against damages resulting from the proceeding.

T   *F*   2. The requirement of an official bond is to protect public funds.

T   *F*   3. Performance bonds always cover unpaid bills of persons performing labor for and furnishing materials to the principal contractor.

T   *F*   4. The creditor is never allowed to subject to the payment of his debt any property given to the surety by the principal debtor as security for the debt.

T   *F*   5. Fidelity bonds are ordinarily entered into by companies to indemnify an employer against loss from the dishonesty or default of an officer, agent, or employee of the employer.

T   *F*   6. The courts unanimously hold that notice of acceptance of a continuing guaranty must be given the guarantor.

Problems. *Analyze each of the following factual situations and state your decision and the reason for your decision in the space provided.*

1. Enumerate some of the most common kinds of judicial bonds.

_____

_____

_____

_____

_____

2. What is the distinction between a surety and an indorser?

_____

_____

_____

_____

_____

_____

_____

3. Brown, the guarantor, addressed a letter "to whom it may concern," promising to pay the debts of Jones, the debtor, if Jones could not pay. Jones purchased certain lumber from The Lumber Company. Jones did not pay for the lumber because of financial reverses, although The Lumber Company continued to make demand for payment. The Lumber Company notified Brown of the default of Jones. Brown contended he was not liable because the letter was not addressed to The Lumber Company. Do you agree with this contention?

_____

_____

_____

_____

_____

_____

_____

4. Aaron, Jr., owed The Office Supply $1,000 for office supplies, and The Office Supply refused to extend further credit to Aaron, Jr. The Office Supply did, however, contemplate bringing an action against Aaron, Jr., to collect the $1,000. Aaron, Sr., then wrote The Office Supply, stating: "If Aaron, Jr., does not pay the $1,000 he owes you by the end of this month, December 31, 1970, I will pay the $1,000 at that time, provided you will not sue my son in the meantime." (a) Is this an absolute guaranty or a conditional guaranty, and (b) what is the liability of Aaron, Sr.?

_____

_____

_____

_____

_____

_____

_____

5. What is the distinction between a surety and an indemnitor?

_____

_____

_____

_____

_____

_____

_____

CHAPTER 61
RIGHTS AND DEFENSES
OF THE SURETY

*Chapter 61 explains, among other things, the rules
pertaining to exoneration, reimbursement, subrogation,
and contribution and the various defenses available to
the surety. You should understand the following after
studying this chapter: the (1) rights of the surety before the creditor has been paid, (2) rights of the surety
after the creditor has been paid, and (3) defenses that
are available to the surety.*

Fill-in Questions. *Write the correct word or words in the blank spaces to
complete the following statements.*

1. The surety has the equitable right of _____
   against the debtor and his cosureties.
2. The right of _____ does not arise until the
   surety has wholly satisfied the debt.
3. A surety who has made payment is entitled to demand _____
   from the principal debtor for the amount which he has paid.
4. A surety is not denied subrogation even though he could have success-
   fully pleaded the statute of _____.
5. The right of _____ exists even though the
   sureties are not aware of the undertaking of each other.
6. A surety who has a right of reimbursement at the time the principal
   debtor is adjudicated a bankrupt must present his claim as a
   _____ against the bankrupt estate.

True-False Questions. *Indicate whether each of the following statements is
true or false by circling the T or F.*

T *F* 1. The decisions are unanimous in holding that a failure on the
            part of the creditor to sue the debtor at maturity discharges
            the surety.
T *F* 2. A surety is given the right of exoneration against his co-
            sureties.
T *F* 3. The surety is discharged if the creditor enters into a volun-
            tary composition with the creditors of the debtor.
T *F* 4. The amount of contribution that a surety can compel from

each of his cosureties is ordinarily determined by the number of solvent sureties within the jurisdiction.

T F 5. Payment before maturity does not entitle the surety to proceed immediately against the principal.

T F 6. The defenses of the debtor—other than those that are entirely personal to the debtor—are, as a general rule, also available to the surety.

T F 7. The majority of the cases hold that the surety is discharged when the security held by the creditor is lost by inactivity of the creditor.

T F 8. A gratuitous extension of time of payment given by the creditor to the debtor will not discharge the surety.

T F 9. The modern-day surety companies must ordinarily show some injury in order to be exonerated.

Problems. Analyze each of the following factual situations and state your decision and the reason for your decision in the space provided.

1. Jones was a surety for an obligation which Jim, an infant, owes to Smith. Jim disaffirmed the contract and returned the consideration. Is Jones discharged?

_____

_____

_____

_____

_____

_____

_____

_____

_____

2. Cabot owed Smith $5,000, and Brown and two others were sureties for the $5,000. The debt became due, and Cabot was financially unable to pay the debt. Must Brown pay the debt before he can compel his cosureties to pay their pro rata share?

_____

_____

_____

3. Bart was a surety for an obligation for $500 which Bridges, the debtor, owed to Bullock, the creditor. Bridges and Bullock entered into an agreement whereby the amount of the obligation was changed to $800. What effect does this change have on the duty of Bart?

4. Brown, the creditor, without the consent of Jones, the surety, gave Smith, the debtor, an extension of thirty days to pay the obligation. Jones contends that he is discharged by the extension. Do you agree with this contention?

5. Adams made a note payable to the order of Cabot for $1,000, which was indorsed by Baker as a guarantor before it was delivered to Cabot as an accommodation for Adams. Baker paid the note after receiving notice that Adams had defaulted. Can Baker recover the sum so paid from Adams?

Name _____ *Date* _____

CHAPTER 62
BANKRUPTCY

Chapter 62 is devoted not only to ordinary bankruptcy but also to corporate reorganizations, arrangements, and wage earners' plans. This chapter is not difficult, but it is rather detailed. You should (1) understand how bankruptcy proceedings are commenced; (2) learn the acts of bankruptcy; (3) understand how the debtor is adjudicated a bankrupt; (4) understand the duties of the referee, the trustee, the receiver, and the appraiser in the administration of the estate of the bankrupt; (5) learn the claims that are provable against the bankrupt's estate and how the trustee may be able to augment the bankrupt's estate; (6) learn the order of payment of provable claims and the effect of the discharge of the proceedings; (7) understand corporate reorganization and arrangements; and (8) learn the rules of an arrangement and wage earners' plans.

Fill-in Questions. *Write the correct word or words in the blank spaces to complete the following statements.*

1. The _____ is the decree of the court which declared the debtor to be a bankrupt.
2. _____ or _____ bankruptcy is a means of liquidation for a debtor hopelessly in debt or for one who desires a liquidation for some reason.
3. The person who is in almost complete charge of the proceedings in bankruptcy is known as the _____.
4. The _____ is a temporary officer whose duty it is to preserve the estate for the creditors until a trustee is elected and qualified.
5. The person who is charged with the actual physical administration of the estate of the bankrupt is known as the _____.
6. A conditional seller who wishes to repossess under his conditional sales contract should file a _____ petition.
7. The major objective of _____ plans is to rehabilitate the wage earner financially and in peace of mind.
8. The plans which involve bankruptcy processes without a liquidation of assets are known as _____ and _____ and _____.

9. A petition for bankruptcy is filed in the federal _____ court.

10. Proofs of claims must be filed by the creditors within _____ months after the first date set for the first meeting of the creditors.

11. A preferential transfer may be recovered by the trustee if the transfer was made by an insolvent debtor within _____ months prior to the filing of the petition in bankruptcy provided the recipient of the preference at the time he received it had reasonable cause to believe that the debtor was insolvent.

12. Tax claims which became due and owing by the bankrupt to the United States or to any state or subdivision thereof within _____ years preceding bankruptcy are not discharged.

13. An arrangement under Chapter XI is designed primarily for individuals and small _____.

14. The petition in involuntary bankruptcy must be filed within _____ months after the commission of the act of bankruptcy by the debtor.

15. In case of involuntary bankruptcy, there must be _____ petitioning creditors if the debtor has twelve or more creditors.

True-False Questions. Indicate whether each of the following statements is true or false by circling the T or F.

T *F* 1. The petition for bankruptcy will be properly filed in the district court where the debtor had his principal place of business or where he resided or had his domicile for the preceding six months.

T *F* 2. The Congress of the United States enacted the Bankruptcy Act in pursuance of its constitutional power.

T *F* 3. Any sane adult debtor may be adjudicated a bankrupt on his own petition.

T *F* 4. Individual farmers and wage earners may be forced into involuntary bankruptcy.

T *F* 5. In case of involuntary bankruptcy, the debtor must have liabilities of $1,200 or more.

T *F* 6. The voluntary petition filed by an individual will operate as an adjudication with the same force and effect as a decree of adjudication.

T *F* 7. Property exemptions allowed by state law are not recognized by the Bankruptcy Act.

T *F* 8. The referee is under a duty to "call" by written notice to all creditors the first meeting of the creditors not less than ten and not more than thirty days after the debtor was adjudicated a bankrupt.

T	*F*	9.	A creditor may participate in a bankruptcy proceeding even though he is unable to prove his claim.
T	*F*	10.	All tort claims are provable in bankruptcy.
T	*F*	11.	Any valid secured lien against the property of the bankrupt continues after the debtor is adjudicated a bankrupt.
T	*F*	12.	The first claim to be paid, other than secured claims, will be the actual and necessary costs and expenses of preserving and administering the estate of the bankrupt.
T	*F*	13.	A debtor is relieved of the payment of all his debts even when he is denied a discharge in bankruptcy.
T	*F*	14.	A wage earner, under Chapter XIII, is not adjudicated a bankrupt.
T	*F*	15.	A wage earner, under Chapter XIII, is not granted a discharge upon proper performance of the plan.

Problems. *Analyze each of the following factual situations and state your decision and the reason for your decision in the space provided.*

1. What is the distinction between the "balance sheet" test and the "equity" test of insolvency?

_____

_____

_____

_____

_____

_____

2. Enumerate the individuals and business organizations that cannot be subjected to involuntary bankruptcy.

_____

_____

_____

_____

_____

_____

3. Brown owed six creditors a total of $5,000, which he was unable to pay. All of the debts were unsecured. If Brown is cautious in not committing an act of bankruptcy, may his creditors force him into involuntary bankruptcy?

_____

_____

_____

_____

_____

_____

4. On January 1, 1970, Brown executed a note payable on July 1, 1971, to the order of Smith for $500. On April 15, 1970, Brown became a voluntary bankrupt. (a) May Smith file a proof of claim? (b) If Smith fails to file a claim, is his claim affected by the discharge of Brown in bankruptcy?

_____

_____

_____

_____

_____

_____

5. Byers owed his father $8,500. He conveyed to his father a tract of land in payment of this debt. At the time of this conveyance, Byers was insolvent, but his father justifiably believed that Byers was solvent and owed no other debts. Three months after this conveyance, Byers was petitioned into bankruptcy by his creditors. May the trustee of Byers avoid this conveyance to the father of Byers and recover the tract of land?

_____

_____

_____

_____

_____

_____

ANSWERS

PART 1: INTRODUCTION

Chapter 1. Nature and Source of Business Law

Fill-in Questions
1. stare decisis
2. ex contractu; ex delicto
3. equity
4. laches
5. accounting
6. partition
7. specific performance
8. quieting title
9. cancellation; rescission
10. injunction
11. law merchant
12. civil
13. public law; private law
14. substantive; adjective; procedural
15. unwritten; written
16. ordinances
17. administrative
18. code

True-False
1. False
2. True
3. True
4. False
5. True
6. False

Answers to Problems

1. It was necessary to organize a court of equity because adhering to precedent became such a habit in early common-law courts of England that later courts were unequal to the task of providing all the rights and remedies necessary in a later and more complex civilization.

2. A few traces of the civil law can be found. With this minor exception, business law in the United States had its origin in the English common-law system of jurisprudence.

3. A few administrative agencies are created by and receive their powers from constitutional provisions. The vast majority of them, however, are created by legislative enactments.

4. Public law is that branch of law which is concerned with the state, including constitutional, administrative, and criminal law. Private law, as used in contradistinction to public law, includes that part of the law which is administered between private individuals.

5. The equitable doctrine of laches. Laches is such delay in asserting a right, taken in conjunction with other circumstances, that the prejudice caused to the other party will operate as a bar for recovery. Laches does not, however, arise from mere

delay or lapse of time. The party against whom laches is sought to be invoked, in addition to the time element, must be aware of his or her rights and fail to assert them.

Chapter 2. The Judicial System

Fill-in Questions
1. supreme
2. foreign
3. appeals
4. personal; constructive
5. district
6. writ; summons
7. supreme
8. jurisdiction
9. pretrial
10. defendant; respondent
11. plaintiff; complainant
12. attachment
13. res judicata
14. execution
15. garnishee

True-False
1. True
2. True
3. False
4. False
5. False
6. False

Answers to Problems

1. The courts of the justices of the peace, the county courts, the circuit courts, and the supreme court of the state.

2. The United States Supreme Court, the courts of appeals, the district courts, and the special courts.

3. The writ of execution in satisfaction of a judgment is not issued until after a money judgment has been rendered. It is also generally held that a writ of execution shall not issue against the property of the defendant for a short time after the judgment has been rendered.

4. The function of the district courts of appeals in the state system of courts is to review decisions rendered in the lower and circuit courts.

5. Jones may ask the court for a writ of attachment. An unsecured creditor may ask for a writ of attachment upon learning that his debtor is planning to abscond or hide his assets.

6. The function of garnishment is to make available for the payment of one's debts certain property which is in the possession of some third person.

7. The record of the lower court, or a history of the case, is filed with the superior court. Both parties then submit briefs consisting of decisions reached in similar cases. The points of error are frequently argued orally before the court. The members of the superior court consider the case, and one member renders the decision for the majority.

Chapter 3. The Nature of Torts and Crimes

Fill-in Questions
1. civil
2. invitor; invitee
3. conversion
4. nuisance
5. battery
6. False
7. defamation; libel; slander
8. deceit

True-False
1. False
2. True
3. True
4. False
5. True
6. True
7. False
8. False

9. replevin
10. crimes

9. True
10. False

Answers to Problems

1. The more significant forms of trespass are trespass to the person, trespass to chattels, and trespass to realty. Assault, battery, and false imprisonment are forms of trespass to persons. Conversion and nuisance are forms of trespass to chattels.

2. Offenses such as murder, arson, and grand larceny are commonly classified as felonies.

3. Offenses such as drunkenness, disorderly conduct, and assault are commonly classified as misdemeanors.

4. Defamation is understood to mean the offense of injuring the reputation of a person by libel or slander. Deceit is the name of the action brought to recover damages for fraud.

5. The test is whether the owner of the appliances receives benefit or advantage from the permitted use by another of that particular appliance or property. If so, the user is an invitee; if not, he is a licensee.

PART 2: CONTRACTS

Chapter 4. Introduction to Contracts

Fill-in Questions
1. quasi
2. void
3. unenforceable
4. executory
5. unilateral
6. express
7. implied in fact
8. bilateral
9. voidable
10. formal
11. valid
12. goods

True-False
1. False
2. False
3. False
4. True
5. True

Answers to Problems

1. Yes. The typewriters would be classified as goods because they are movable at the time of identification to the contract for sale.

2. A contractual relationship will be created when the ring is found and returned to Mary.

3. Aaron would not be permitted to bring an action on February 1, 1978. The lawnmower would be classified as goods, and the statutory period of time for bringing an action is four years in a sale of goods.

4. No. The contract is void. The objective of the contract was illegal.

5. An agreement, both offer and acceptance, supported by consideration, entered into by parties having capacity to contract, the objective of which is legal.

Chapter 5. Agreement

Fill-in Questions
1. merchants
2. bidder

True-False
1. True
2. False

3. communicated	3. True
4. offeror	4. True
5. offeree	5. False
6. option	6. False
7. manifestation	7. True
8. negotiate	8. False
9. continuing	9. True
10. insanity	10. True
11. unilateral	11. False
12. firm	12. True
13. reasonable	13. True
14. counteroffer	14. False

Answers to Problems

1. No. The contract is too indefinite. The time of performance was stated in such a vague and uncertain manner that the intention of Butler could not be determined.

2. The Hardware Company could bring an action for a reasonable price. The tractors would be classified as goods, and no contract price had been previously agreed upon. The price was to be agreed upon by Cabot and The Hardware Company, but they failed to agree upon the price.

3. No. Blackacre was not advertised "without reserve." The auctioneer may therefore withdraw the property at any time prior to acceptance of the bid.

4. None. Bob was not an agent for Adams. The acceptance of an offer can only be made by the offeree, and Adams did not accept the offer.

5. (1) The books would be classified as goods, and the Code provides that the auctioneer in his discretion may either reopen the bidding or accept the bid on which the hammer was falling as the closing bid. (2) Smith, the seller, must give notice that he intends to make bids at the auction. Brown has the option of avoiding the sale or taking the last good-faith bid.

6. Yes. The offer of Mary did not specify a definite time of duration. The offer, therefore, lapsed after a reasonable time.

7. No. The beginning of the requested performance was a reasonable mode of acceptance, and the Code provides that the offeror—The Cabinet Shop—may treat the offer as lapsed unless the offeree—Brown—notifies the offeror that the offer has been accepted.

8. No. This was an output contract. The seller did not operate his plant in good faith and according to commercial standards of fair dealing of the trade.

9. Yes. Baker failed to designate a transmitting agency. It is therefore implied that Jones is authorized to use the same medium of transmission as Baker used for the offer. The contract was formed as soon as the letter of acceptance was mailed.

10. A requirement contract is one whereby the buyer promises to purchase all his requirements from the seller in exchange for the promise of the seller to supply all the needs of the buyer. An output contract is one whereby the seller promises to sell all his production to the buyer in exchange for the promise of the buyer to purchase all the output of the seller.

Chapter 6. Consideration

Fill-in Questions

1. mutual
2. promisee
3. estoppel
4. rescission

True-False

1. True
2. True
3. False
4. True

5. good
6. Promissory
7. waiver
8. past
9. liquidated
10. adequate
11. promisor
12. accord; satisfaction
13. compromise; settlement

5. True
6. False
7. False
8. True
9. True
10. False
11. True

Answers to Problems

1. No. Jones promised to perform, but he reserved to himself the option to perform or not to perform. The promise is not enforceable, because there is no promise to enforce.

2. No. The father's promise, which is made for a "past consideration," is not sufficient to make the contract enforceable.

3. Yes. When Rogers agreed to finish and did finish the construction by April 15, rather than May 1, he, as promisee, suffered a new legal detriment which made the promise of Barsh enforceable.

4. Decision for Brown, Jr. This was a "good consideration," which is not sufficient to make a contract enforceable. It was, however, an executed gift. An executed gift cannot be set aside because of the absence of consideration.

5. Yes. The Code provides that an agreement modifying a contract, if made in good faith, needs no consideration to be enforceable.

Chapter 7. Capacity of Parties

Fill-in Questions
1. disaffirmance
2. necessaries
3. majority
4. tortious
5. voidable
6. real estate
7. incompetent
8. emancipated
9. ratify; disaffirm
10. ratification

True-False
1. False
2. True
3. False
4. True
5. False
6. True
7. False
8. False

Answers to Problems

1. No. Taylor had a voidable title because Barsh was an infant. The Code provides, however, that a person with a voidable title has the power to transfer a good title to a good faith purchaser for value.

2. Yes. The infant, after reaching his majority, promptly disaffirmed the contract. He was, therefore, free to sell to someone else. Jones, dealing with an adult, had a good contractual claim.

3. Decision for the guardian. Goods which are necessaries in themselves cease to be necessaries when the party concerned has an ample supply. This is one of the risks that the seller has to assume in dealing with an infant.

4. Decision for the pedestrian. A minor is liable for his torts and can be sued if he injures another or another's property.

5. No. He disaffirmed the contract when he moved out of the apartment. Any words or acts by the infant which clearly indicate an intent to repudiate the contract

will operate as a disaffirmance. The apartment was a necessary for Staley as long as he occupied the apartment. It ceased to be a necessary, however, when he vacated the apartment.

Chapter 8. Illegality

Fill-in Questions
1. blue
2. usury
3. ancillary
4. pari delicto
5. monopolize
6. Truth-in-Lending
7. wager
8. divisible

True-False
1. False
2. False
3. False
4. True
5. True
6. False

Answers to Problems

1. Yes. The agreement was to defeat the creditors of Baker, Sr., but Baker, Sr., was not equally guilty. In those cases where the parties are not in pari delicto, the law will render relief to the more innocent party.

2. No. The Federal Consumer Credit Protection Act covers intrastate as well as interstate transactions unless the particular state has enacted a statute similar to the Truth-in-Lending Act.

3. Yes. Brown and the Acme Company were not in pari delicto. The law permits one party who innocently or through a mistake of fact participates in an illegal contract to recover from the other party.

4. Yes. A loan made in violation of a statute would be illegal, but the courts, in order to carry out the purpose of the statute, would enforce the contract and require Taylor to repay the loan.

Chapter 9. Reality of Consent

Fill-in Questions
1. silence
2. deceit
3. opinion
4. duress
5. unconscionable
6. mutual
7. influence
8. expert
9. unilateral
10. scienter

True-False
1. False
2. True
3. True
4. False
5. True
6. True
7. True
8. False
9. True
10. True

Answers to Problems

1. No. Brown made a false representation, but Jones did not rely on the representation. Fraud will not result unless the misrepresentation is relied upon by the injured party.

2. No. The brother used undue influence in inducing Mary to sign the agreement, and the officers of the First Bank were a party to the agreement. A contract entered into under circumstances which show that one person took unfair advantage of another because of superior knowledge derived from a fiduciary relationship or from overmastering influence may be rescinded.

3. No. The statement of Brown would not amount to actionable fraud. There was no intention to deceive, and the statement was not of a past or present fact. Brown simply breached his promise.

4. No. This was a unilateral mistake which was the result of the negligence of Roberts. The contractor acted in good faith without notice or knowledge of the mistake, and a party to a contract cannot avoid it on the ground that he made a mistake when the other party had no notice of the mistake and acted in good faith.

5. No. The acts of Cabot amounted to a misrepresentation of a material fact, which was the location of the land. A misrepresentation of a fact is material if it induces a person to enter into a contract that he would not have entered into except for the misrepresentation. Davis may have the contract rescinded because of the misrepresentation.

Chapter 10. Contracts Required to Be in Writing

Fill-in Questions	True-False
1. guaranty	1. True
2. special; collateral	2. False
3. quasi	3. False
4. specially	4. True
5. quantity	5. False
6. executor	6. True
7. marry	7. False
8. year	8. True
9. formal	9. True
10. collection	10. True

Answers to Problems

1. By giving written notice of objection to the seller within ten days after receipt of the confirmation.

2. No. This contract could not be performed within a year from the time it was made. The Statute of Frauds requires that the note or memorandum must be signed by the party sought to be charged. Brown, the party sought to be charged, did not sign the memorandum.

3. Yes. Brown can recover from Baker because Baker, the party sought to be charged, signed the memorandum.

4. No. An oral contract for the sale of goods is enforceable if the party against whom enforcement is sought makes a statement in court admitting that he has entered into a contract. The contract would be enforceable for $4,500, the amount admitted.

5. No. Brown's promise to pay the debt was not a collateral promise. It was, on the other hand, an original promise since Brown made the debt his own. Brown promised to pay the $5,000 to the X Wholesale Company in order to benefit himself. He is, therefore, liable on the oral promise.

6. The promise is not required to be in writing. If the promisor has an immediate business or pecuniary interest in the transaction to the extent that he obtains a substantial benefit to himself, the promise is an original one, without the statute, and is not required to be in writing to be enforceable.

Chapter 11. Rights of Third Parties

Fill-in Questions	True-False
1. beneficiary	1. True
2. creditor	2. True

3. warrants
4. incidental
5. assignee
6. notice
7. first
8. personal services
9. benefits; burdens
10. promisor

3. False
4. False
5. True
6. False
7. True
8. True

Answers to Problems

1. The clause would be ineffective insofar as the right to the payment of money was concerned but would prohibit the delegation of the performance of the duties of the assignor to the assignee.

2. This would constitute an assignment of rights and a delegation of the performance of the duties of Brown.

3. Yes. The son named in the policy is the third-party donee. The son could not be a creditor beneficiary because the father was not indebted to him.

4. No. The bank agreed to lend $5,000 to Jones on the basis of the personal qualifications of Jones. The bank may not be willing to accept Kelly as a credit risk. Contract rights of such a personal nature may not be assigned.

5. No. Most courts hold that contracting parties who have entered into a contract for the benefit of a third person may not rescind the contract after it has been acted upon by the third party.

Chapter 12. Performance

Fill-in Questions
1. concurrent
2. Substantial
3. precedent
4. essence
5. partial
6. indivisible; divisible
7. specific
8. subsequent

True-False
1. True
2. False
3. False
4. True
5. True
6. True
7. True
8. False
9. False

Answers to Problems

1. No. If performance is such that it must satisfy the personal satisfaction of another person, the latter's own determination—if made in good faith—is final and conclusive when the contract has to do with personal taste and fancy.

2. Yes. A contract which, at the time it is entered into, is impossible to perform is void; there is no contract to discharge. The same result could be reached on the basis of a mutual mistake of a material fact.

3. No. This was a condition precedent. Performance by Drake must occur before there is a duty of immediate performance by David.

4. No. Time was not of the essence of the contract. The contract, moreover, was substantially performed.

5. No. This was impossibility created by law. A contract which is legal in its inception but which becomes illegal by subsequent statutory enactment is terminated as soon as the statute becomes effective.

Chapter 13. Remedies, Damages, Interpretation

Fill-in Questions
1. interpretation
2. rescission
3. Specific performance
4. injunction
5. primary; secondary
6. penalty
7. parol evidence
8. prior; contemporaneous
9. nominal
10. general
11. written

True-False
1. True
2. True
3. False
4. False
5. True
6. False
7. True
8. False

Answers to Problems

1. Yes. This is not a contract for the breach of which the injured party can be compensated in money damages. Specific performance will be granted, therefore, because more complete justice can be accomplished by requiring performance of the contract.

2. This is an anticipatory breach. The Code provides that the manufacturer has the option of completing manufacture or ceasing manufacture. If he completes manufacture, he may resell the goods. If he ceases manufacture, he may resell the partially manufactured goods for scrap or salvage. He may recover as damages any loss from such resale. If resale is not practicable, he may bring an action for the price.

3. Yes. Davis was guilty of deceit—fraud—which gives the injured party, Brown, an election of remedies, including rescission. Total rescission restores the parties to the status quo.

4. No. Specific performance is not allowed for personal services; to enforce such contracts would be unconstitutional.

5. Baker can recover $200 as general damages, which damages resulted directly from the breach, and $10,000 as special damages. The party injured by the breach of the contract is entitled to recover special damages which arise from circumstances peculiar to the case. The special damages, however, must be communicated to, or at least known by, the other party at the time the contract is entered into. Adams knew the purpose for which Baker contracted to buy the harvester.

Chapter 14. Discharge of Contracts

Fill-in Questions
1. novation
2. tender
3. breach
4. anticipatory
5. limitations
6. bankruptcy
7. merger
8. account stated
9. Arbitration
10. covenant
11. submission; submit to arbitration

True-False
1. True
2. False
3. True
4. True
5. False
6. True
7. False
8. True

Answers to Problems

1. No. This was a merger. The judgment awarded to the store discharged by merger the right of action on the open account.

2. Material alteration. An intentional material alteration will ordinarily discharge any contract in writing.

3. No. Baker's remedy would be to bring an action for breach of contract. A covenant never to sue on a joint obligation will not release any of the joint obligors.

4. Yes. This was an anticipatory breach, and Brown could have brought an action on December 10, 1970. He elected, however, to treat the contract as binding. Brown is now in breach of contract.

PART 3: SALES

Chapter 15. Sales: Introduction

Fill-in Questions
1. goods
2. future
3. fungible
4. shipment; destination
5. c.o.d.; f.o.b.; f.a.s.; c.i.f.
6. entrusted
7. sale or return
8. sale on approval
9. ordinary course of business

True-False
1. True
2. True
3. False
4. False
5. True
6. True
7. True
8. False
9. False
10. True
11. True
12. False
13. True

Answers to Problems

1. The dealer. This was a destination contract, and the dealer is under a duty to transport the goods to Jacksonville, Florida, and make a proper tender of delivery at his own expense and risk.

2. No. This would be a shipment contract. The dealer would be under a duty to bear the expense and risk of putting the goods into the possession of the carrier.

3. Brown. Defendant was a merchant, and retention of possession for one day would be a reasonable time. The Code provides that it is not fraudulent against creditors for a merchant-seller to retain possession of the goods in good faith for a commercially reasonable time.

4. This was fungible goods, and Jones and Smith must share the loss proportionately. Jones must share one-third of the loss, and Smith must share two-thirds of the loss. The risk of loss passed to the buyers when the negotiable warehouse receipts were delivered to them.

5. To prevent dealers from selling their merchandise in bulk and departing with the money received without paying their creditors.

Chapter 16. Sales: Warranties

Fill-in Questions
1. title
2. suitability
3. merchantability

True-False
1. True
2. False
3. False

4. caveat emptor
5. usage of trade
6. implied warranty; refused
7. caveat venditor
8. sales talk; puffing
9. modification
10. entirety clause
11. privity
12. statements of opinion; statements of fact

4. True
5. True
6. False
7. True
8. False

Answers to Problems

1. A sale by sample is created when the seller actually draws a sample from the bulk of the goods; a sale by model is created when the seller offers a model for inspection when the goods are not readily available; a sale by description may be made by patent name, trade name, blueprints, and the like.

2. Yes. The Code gives the buyer's family, household, and guests, as beneficiaries, the benefit of the same warranty which the buyer receives in the contract of sale. Tomatoes which make a person ill obviously are not merchantable.

3. Decision for the auctioneer. An auctioneer does not impliedly warrant the title. He is a person who sells not in his own right as owner but in the right of another.

4. No. Statements which are the opinion or the belief only of the seller, commonly referred to as "sales talk" or "puffing," are permissible in the law of sales.

5. No. (1) The seller did not use the word "merchantable." (2) The disclaimer was made orally, and to exclude a warranty of fitness for a particular purpose, the disclaimer must be by a writing and be conspicuous. (3) The seller did not use specific language.

Chapter 17. Sales: Performance

Fill-in Questions
1. conforming
2. nonnegotiable
3. banking
4. commercial
5. documentary sale
6. merchant
7. cure; cure
8. assurances

True-False
1. True
2. False
3. True
4. False
5. False
6. False
7. True
8. False
9. False
10. True
11. True
12. True
13. False
14. True

Answers to Problems

1. No. The buyer may accept all of the goods, reject all of the goods, or he may accept any commercial unit and reject the rest provided the goods fail to conform to the contract in any respect. If he accepted, he could revoke his acceptance.

2. No. The buyer could not reject the engine, since a truck is one commercial unit.

3. No. The seller may demand cash, but he must allow the buyer a reasonable time in which to cure by procuring the cash.

4. No. The seller is excused from delivering the goods where his performance has become impracticable because of an unforeseen contingency not within the contemplation of the parties at the time they entered into the contract.

5. The buyer may suspend his own performance until the situation is clarified; he may make written demand for adequate assurances of performance; or he may treat the contract as broken if the seller fails to provide adequate assurances within a reasonable time—not to exceed thirty days—after receipt of the demand.

6. (1) The seller must tender and the buyer must accept transportation when the agreed method of transportation becomes impracticable but where commercially reasonable substitute transportation is available. (2) The seller is given the right to withhold or stop delivery of the goods unless the buyer provides a substantially equivalent manner of payment.

Chapter 18. Sales: Remedies

Fill-in Questions	True-False
1. insolvency; breach of contract	1. True
2. carload, truckload, planeload; larger	2. True
3. cancellation; rescission	3. False
4. reclaim	4. False
5. cover	5. True
6. revocation	6. True
7. recoupment	7. False
8. suspend; anticipatory	8. False
	9. True
	10. True

Answers to Problems

1. Yes. The seller has the right to stop the goods in transit when he learns of the insolvency of the buyer.

2. Yes. The First Bank had advanced the money to the buyer for the purpose of purchasing the goods. The First Bank, therefore, was a "person in the position of the seller."

3. The wholesaler could reclaim the remaining unsold TV sets from the Warehouse Company. He obviously could not stop the TV sets in transit because they had been delivered to The Warehouse Company.

4. No. The buyer is given the right to reach the goods on the insolvency of the seller. The buyer had an insurable interest in the typewriter, and the insolvency occurred within ten days after the buyer paid the first installment.

5. No. The buyer may ordinarily revoke his acceptance, but he must do so within a reasonable time. Plaintiff discovered the nonconformity two weeks after the corn was received, but he waited for six months before he notified defendant that the corn was nonconforming. It was then too late to revoke his acceptance. Plaintiff could, however, recover damages for nonconformity.

PART 4: COMMERCIAL PAPER

Chapter 19. Nature of Commercial Paper

Fill-in Questions	True-False
1. negotiable	1. False
2. law merchant	2. True
3. promissory note	3. True

4. maker
5. mortgage notes
6. coupon; registered
7. payee
8. collateral
9. trade acceptance
10. clean; documentary
11. certificate of deposit
12. bank; bank; bank
13. traveler's
14. title-retaining
15. draft
16. drawee

4. True
5. False
6. True
7. False
8. False

Chapter 20. Form and Interpretation

Fill-in Questions
1. promise
2. demand; definite time
3. order; bearer
4. certain
5. acceleration
6. unconditional
7. confession
8. order
9. antedated; undated
10. satisfaction
11. particular
12. money

True-False
1. True
2. False
3. True
4. False
5. True
6. False
7. False
8. True
9. False
10. True
11. False
12. True
13. False
14. False
15. False
16. True
17. False
18. True
19. False
20. False
21. True
22. True
23. True
24. False

Answers to Problems

1. No. The sum is not rendered uncertain by a promise to pay a different rate of interest before and after maturity. The amount due at maturity is certain.

2. Bearer paper. The Code provides that an instrument is payable to bearer when by its terms it is payable to "cash" or to the order of "cash."

3. No. Mere recitals in instruments, such as "this note is given to secure the payment of" a certain automobile will not make the promise or order conditional.

4. No. Drafts may be addressed to one or more drawees jointly or in the alternative. The person being ordered (commanded) to pay must be identified with reasonable certainty. This alone would destroy negotiability in this problem, because in Miami, Florida, there could easily be a number of persons by the name of Ben Roberts and Tom Brown.

5. Make the time of payment certain; for example, "thirty days after date pay to the order of . . ."; identify the drawees with reasonable certainty by adding their street addresses.

6. $300.50. Words control figures, but figures control if the words are ambiguous.

7. No. An instrument is payable at a definite time if it is payable at a definite time subject to any acceleration.

8. No. This note does not contain words of negotiability. The words "order" or "bearer" are not used and no other similar words are used.

9. The quoted provision does not destroy negotiability. The quoted words are treated as payable to the order of the appropriate representative.

10. (a) bearer paper; (b) bearer paper; (c) incomplete order paper; (d) order paper; (e) bearer paper.

Chapter 21. Transfer and Negotiation

Fill-in Questions
1. Negotiation
2. allonge
3. blank
4. restrictive
5. special
6. transferee
7. indorser
8. indorsee or holder
9. without recourse

True-False
1. False
2. True
3. False
4. False
5. True
6. True
7. True
8. False

Answers to Problems

1. No. The payee, in order to properly negotiate the note, must indorse the note and deliver it to the indorsee. Boles is not an indorsee; he is a transferee who acquired the rights of the payee and, in addition, the right to have the indorsement of the payee.

2. A restrictive indorsement which creates an agency. "Pay to the First Bank for collection only. The XYZ Store, by Jan Baker, Manager."

3. No. A negotiation is effective to transfer the instrument although the negotiation is made by any person without capacity. An infant may negotiate the instrument so as to constitute his transferee a holder and the indorsee may further negotiate the instrument to a holder in due course. An infant cannot then recover the instrument from the holder in due course.

4. No. The Code provides, in effect, that any instrument which is specially indorsed requires the indorsement of the special indorsee for further negotiation. Adams did not indorse.

5. No. This is not a proper negotiation. The Code provides that when an allonge is used, the paper must be so firmly affixed thereto so as to become a part thereof. In this problem, a proper indorsement should have been on the note.

Chapter 22. Holders in Due Course

Fill-in Questions
1. security interest
2. irrevocable
3. value; overdue; dishonored; defense; claim; good faith
4. demand or presentment

True-False
1. False
2. False
3. True
4. True

5. dishonored
6. Good faith
7. fiduciary
8. reacquirer

5. True
6. True
7. False
8. True
9. False
10. True

Answers to Problems

1.

$250.00	Boston, Mass. (Month) (Day)	19(Year)

On July 1, 1970 - - - - - - - - - - - - - - - - - - - Pay to the order of

Tom Bryan -

Two Hundred Fifty and No/100ths - - - - - - - - - - - - - - Dollars

Value rec'd and charge to account of

To   Bob Clark
        1234 Main Street   Jack Kelley
        Los Angeles, Calif.   By: (Signature of Agent), Agent

2. No. Knowledge that there has been a default in the payment of interest would not prevent the holder from taking as a holder in due course. Interest payments are frequently delayed.

3. Yes. Brown had notice of a claim or defense when he purchased with notice that the obligation of Baker was voidable—Acme refused to deliver the TV set.

4. No. Black could be a holder in due course unless he had knowledge that the option to accelerate has been exercised.

5. No. The "subject to" clause renders this note nonnegotiable. The purchaser would be a holder in due course if the note had been negotiable.

6. The decision would be for Taylor since the instrument is nonnegotiable. The words of negotiability are missing. If it were negotiable, John could not be a holder in due course since he did not pay value for the note. With respect to the blank after "19," the Code provides that the purchaser would have notice of a claim or defense if the instrument is so irregular as to call into question its validity. The Code does not require that paper be "complete and regular," but this is taken into consideration in determining whether the taker is one in good faith. It is believed that the blank in this case, standing alone, would not prevent a purchaser from purchasing in good faith.

Chapter 23. Defenses

Fill-in Questions
1. personal; real
2. Real
3. excusably
4. immediate
5. personal
6. defense
7. inducement
8. execution
9. material
10. authorization
11. negligence
12. personal

True-False
1. False
2. True
3. True
4. True
5. True
6. False
7. False
8. False
9. True
10. False
11. True
12. True

Answers to Problems

1. None. Delivery of an incomplete instrument is a personal defense, which cannot be asserted against a holder in due course.

2. Delivery of an incomplete instrument, which may be asserted as between the immediate parties.

3. No. Nondelivery of a completed instrument is a personal defense which is cut off in the hands of a holder in due course.

4. Yes. Nondelivery of an incomplete instrument is a personal defense. The maker should stand the loss rather than the innocent purchaser.

5. Sims can recover the full amount of the note, i.e., $100. Fraud in the inducement—consideration—is a personal defense. Sims, a holder in due course, holds the note free of this defense.

6. No. The words of negotiability—to order or to bearer—are lacking and the instrument is nonnegotiable. Sims would be a mere holder of a nonnegotiable note, and he would therefore be subject to the defense of fraud in the consideration.

Chapter 24. Presentment, Notice of Dishonor, Protest

Fill-in Questions

1. excused; excused
2. bank-domiciled
3. protest
4. notice of dishonor
5. face
6. conditions precedent
7. three-day rule
8. west; south

True-False

1. False
2. False
3. True
4. True
5. False
6. True
7. True
8. False
9. True
10. False

Answers to Problems

1. No. The conditions of presentment, protest, and notice of dishonor are for the protection of the drawer and indorsers. This protection, therefore, may be waived. The waiver, when written across the face of the instrument, is binding upon all parties. A waiver, however, is sometimes written above the signature of one of the indorsers. It might be added that in this problem, presentment and notice of dishonor are "entirely excused."

2. Drake has a right to recover from Baker. A prompt presentment is not necessary to obligate a maker to pay the instrument. The maker (primary party) will remain liable on the instrument during the entire period of the statute of limitations after a default. The presentment must be made in a proper form by the holder to the person primarily liable, at a proper place, and at a proper time, and proper notice must be given to the secondary parties of the dishonor. Any indorser to whom such notice is not given is discharged. Cabot is, therefore, discharged by the failure of Drake to present the note on the date of maturity for payment.

3. Written notice of dishonor is given when sent although it is not received.

4. This was not a proper presentment. The presentment is invalidated if the person making the presentment fails to exhibit the instrument when he is requested to do so. This was not, however, a dishonor.

5. (1) Where the draft expressly stipulates that it shall be presented for acceptance; (2) Where the draft is drawn payable elsewhere than at the residence or place of business of the drawee; and (3) Where the draft is payable after sight or in any other case where presentment for acceptance is necessary in order to fix the maturity of the instrument.

Chapter 25. Liability of Parties

Fill-in Questions
1. contractual
2. primarily
3. surety
4. payor; acceptor
5. drawers; indorsers
6. payor; acceptor
7. transferor
8. without recourse
9. payee; indorse
10. accommodated
11. face-to-face; mail

True-False
1. True
2. False
3. True
4. True
5. True
6. False
7. True
8. False
9. True
10. True

Answers to Problems

1. No. Ben Adams is a special qualified indorser. He warrants that he has no knowledge of any defense of any party that is good against him. There was no breach of warranty. Adams disclaimed his liability on the contract of indorsement by writing the words "without recourse" on the instrument. Adams would have to pay Brown if the indorsement had not included the words "without recourse."

2. No. Adams is personally liable. An unauthorized agent who signs an instrument in the name of the principal and a forger are personally liable on the instrument.

3. Yes. The Code expressly covers the situation of alteration. A qualified, as well as an unqualified, indorser warrants that the instrument had not been materially altered. Adams, a qualified indorser, is liable.

4. Yes. Jim Jones should have identified Mary Jones as the principal. Jim Jones cannot use parol evidence to disestablish his obligation because the controversy is not between the immediate parties.

5. No. The acceptor is liable. Assuming that Brown is a holder in due course, the presentment warranty against forgery would not be imposed against him if he took the instrument and then, without knowledge of the forgery, procured the acceptance. In this problem, Cabot is a holder in due course and he certainly can recover from the acceptor. The Code provides that the warranty is not given by a holder in due course acting in good faith.

6. The corporation. The indorsement by Brown was effective to transfer the instrument. The test is whether the signer intended that the named payee should have no interest in the instrument.

Chapter 26. Discharge

Fill-in Questions
1. restrictive
2. reacquires
3. material; fraudulent
4. holder in due course
5. Cancellation
6. Renunciation

True-False
1. True
2. True
3. True
4. False
5. False

Answers to Problems

1. No. Cancellation is inoperative if it is made unintentionally, under a mistake, or without the authority of the holder. In order to effectually discharge an instrument by cancellation, the cancellation must be written on the instrument itself or the instrument must be destroyed.

2. Yes. The indorsement of Jones was not cancelled by striking. Jones is, therefore, liable to a holder in due course.

3. Yes. No discharge of any party is effective against a holder in due course unless the holder in due course has notice of the discharge when he takes the instrument. Jay had no knowledge of the agreement between Baker and Abel.

4. No. Smith was justified in paying the holder of the note on the date of maturity, although he had knowledge of a claim to the note on the part of a third person. Payment to the holder discharges the paying party.

5. No. Cobb was a reacquirer. Intervening parties are discharged where a prior holder reacquires the instrument.

Chapter 27. Relationship between Payor Bank and Its Customer

Fill-in Questions	True-False
1. special; general	1. True
2. on us	2. True
3. Certification	3. False
4. subrogation	4. False
5. creditor; debtor	5. False
6. statute of limitations	6. True
7. stale	7. True
	8. False
	9. True

Answers to Problems

1. No. The check was deposited within a reasonable time. The Code provides that a check should be deposited within thirty days to hold the drawer liable or assume the risk of the payor bank's insolvency.

2. No. The Code provides that the bank must pay or dishonor a check before the close of business on the day of presentment where such check is presented over the counter for immediate payment.

3. No. The Code expressly gives the bank the right to pay checks for a period of ten days even though the bank has notice of the death of the drawer.

4. The reason is that persons other than the drawer could telephone a stop order to the bank. It is difficult to identify some persons over the telephone.

PART 5: BAILMENTS; DOCUMENTS OF TITLE

Chapter 28. Bailments

Fill-in Questions	True-False
1. bailor	1. False
2. custody	2. True
3. bailor; bailee	3. True
4. bailee	4. True
5. mutual benefit	5. True
6. gratuitous	6. False
7. destroyed	7. False
8. factor's	8. False
9. artisan's	9. True
10. consignor	10. False
11. consignee	
12. consignment	

Answers to Problems

1. Yes. The bailee will be liable for any loss which results from using the bailed property in a different place from that which was intended.

2. Brown. The bailee of a horse for hire would be required to pay the usual expenses of housing and feeding, but extraordinary expenses, such as veterinarian services due to an unexpected illness of the horse, should be borne by the bailor.

3. Yes. The bailor and the bailee, both of whom have a property interest in the bailed goods, can recover damages from a wrongful third person for conversion or damages inflicted.

4. The Repair Shop. The Repair Shop had an artisan's lien. The Code provides that an artisan's lien takes priority over an earlier security interest where the services are furnished in the ordinary course of business and the goods are in the artisan's possession. The Code, however, does not repeal statutory provisions which expressly make the artisan's lien subordinate to prior liens.

5. Yes. This was not a bailment, because Baker was under no duty to return the identical sheep. A sale results where there is an agreement to pay money or its equivalent for the thing delivered, and the receiving party is under no obligation to return the specific thing or to account for it. The loss, if any, will fall on Baker. Baker is under a duty to deliver ten sheep to Adams as well as the agreed wool.

Chapter 29. Documents of Title, Carriers, Warehousemen

Fill-in Questions	True-False
1. bill of lading; warehouse receipt	1. False
2. bailee	2. True
3. storing goods for hire	3. False
4. transporting; forwarding	4. True
5. through	5. True
6. freight forwarder	6. False
7. destination	7. True
8. nonnegotiable	8. True
9. retain control; carrier	9. True
10. negotiable	10. True
11. indorsement; delivery	11. True
12. good faith; authority	12. False
13. strict	13. False
14. shipper's weight, load, and count	14. True
15. agreed valuation	15. True

Answers to Problems

1. Yes. The indorser of a negotiable document impliedly warrants, among other things, that the document is genuine and that he has no knowledge of any fact that would impair the validity of it.

2. The warehouseman may terminate the storage by giving notice of the termination, which may take effect not less than thirty days after notification of the termination. The warehouseman may then sell the goods by public or private sale if the goods are not removed at the end of the period.

3. The goods may arrive at the destination before the document would ordinarily arrive, and no one would be ready to take delivery from the carrier.

4. Brown could ask the court to authorize the delivery of the goods or the issuance of a substitute document. The warehouse receipt was negotiable. Brown could, however, post a security bond approved by the court.

5. Decision for the Smiths. The Transfer and Storage Company lost its lien. The lien of the carrier is a possessory lien, and the carrier loses his lien if he voluntarily delivers the goods.

6. The Code provides that the warehouseman may terminate the storage by giving notice to all persons known to have an interest in the goods when the goods are hazardous.

7. No. The warehouseman lost his lien with respect to the goods stored in April when he voluntarily surrendered the goods to Brown. The warehouseman could have, however, claimed a general lien at the time the goods were stored in June by inserting on the warehouse receipt a recital that "a lien is claimed for charges and expenses in relation to other goods."

8. No. The Code provides that a buyer in the ordinary course of business of fungible goods sold and delivered by a warehouseman who is also in the business of buying and selling such goods takes free of any claim under a warehouse receipt even though it has been duly negotiated.

9. (1) Acts of God; (2) acts of the public enemy; (3) acts of public authorities; (4) acts of the shipper; (5) inherent nature of the goods.

10. (1) Delivery of the goods to a person whose warehouse receipt was rightful as against the claimant; (2) Damage to or delay, loss or destruction of the goods for which the bailee is not liable; (3) Exercise by a seller of his right to stop the goods in transit under the law of sales; (4) A diversion or reconsignment of the goods; (5) Any other lawful excuse.

PART 6: SECURED TRANSACTIONS

Chapter 30. Secured Transactions: Introduction

Fill-in Questions
1. consumer goods
2. equipment
3. farm products
4. inventory
5. accounts
6. account
7. general intangibles
8. document
9. instrument
10. chattel paper
11. secured party; debtor; collateral; security agreement; security interest

True-False
1. False
2. True
3. True
4. True
5. True
6. True
7. True
8. True
9. False
10. False
11. True
12. True
13. True
14. True

Chapter 31. The Security Interest

Fill-in Questions
1. attachment
2. perfection
3. notice filing
4. central
5. financing statement
6. proceeds
7. deposit account

True-False
1. False
2. True
3. False
4. True
5. True
6. True
7. False

8. five years	8. False
9. last event	9. True
10. last event	10. False
11. debtor	11. True
	12. False
	13. False
	14. True
	15. True
	16. False
	17. True

Answers to Problems

1. Yes. If the secured party perfects his security interest in the collateral by filing a financing statement, permanent perfection in the proceeds will be automatic in most instances. The definition of the word "proceeds" in section 9–306 is broad enough to include insurance which is payable as a result of loss of or damage to the collateral, unless the insurance contract designates a beneficiary who is not a party to the security agreement.

2. No. It is deficient in that it does not contain the address of The Finance Company. One of the formal requisites of the financing statement is that it contain the name and address of both the debtor and the secured party. A claim to the proceeds is not required.

3. Adams. Aaron failed to file a continuation statement. The perfection of the financing statement, therefore, lapsed at the end of five years.

4. No. The Code expressly provides that a security interest is not invalid or fraudulent against creditors by use of the debtor to use, commingle, or dispose of all or a part of the collateral.

5. No. The duration of perfection is effective for a period of five years after the date of filing. The duration of perfection will not terminate, although no continuation statement is filed, when a real estate mortgage is filed as a fixture filing. The real estate mortgage, which is a fixture filing, is still valid.

Chapter 32. Priorities and Remedies

Fill-in Questions

1. lien
2. artisan's
3. purchase-money
4. accession
5. real estate
6. cash; noncash
7. surplus; deficiency
8. commercially
9. time
10. after-acquired
11. ten
12. identifiable cash
13. fixtures
14. fixture
15. real estate
16. purchase-money

True-False

1. True
2. True
3. True
4. False
5. False
6. False
7. True
8. True
9. False
10. True
11. False
12. False
13. False
14. True
15. True
16. False
17. True
18. False
19. True
20. False

Answers to Problems

1. A purchase-money security interest will arise (1) when the seller sells goods to the buyer and retains a security interest in the goods, (2) when a lender advances money to the seller and takes back an assignment of the chattel paper, and (3) when a lender advances money to the buyer—for instance, on a chattel mortgage—to enable the buyer to buy the goods, and the buyer uses the money for that purpose.

2. The Second Bank. The Second Bank was a second financer, but the Second Bank gave new value and took possession of the chattel paper in the ordinary course of business. This is true even though the Second Bank knew that the specific paper was subject to the security interest of the inventory financer. This rule governs the situation where the security interest in chattel paper or instruments is claimed merely as proceeds by the inventory financer.

3. No. The security interest of the First Bank was cut off when the goods were sold to Brown. The rights of an inventory financer will be cut off when the goods are resold to a buyer in the ordinary course of business.

4. No. The furniture was equipment, and Brown perfected his security interest. A purchase-money security interest in collateral other than inventory is given priority over a conflicting security interest if the security interest is perfected at the time the debtor receives possession of the collateral or within ten days thereafter.

5. A secured party who wishes to leave the chattel paper or instrument—the collateral—in the possession of the debtor should protect himself against purchasers by stamping or noting on the paper in such a way as to indicate the outstanding security interest.

6. The secured party may, unless he is compelled to sell the collateral, propose in writing to retain the collateral in satisfaction of the obligation. If he chooses this alternative, he must notify the debtor only in case of consumer goods if the debtor has not signed a statement after default in which he renounced or modified his rights.

PART 7: AGENCY

Chapter 33. Creation and Authority

Fill-in Questions
1. independent contractor
2. agent
3. factor
4. necessity
5. Actual
6. incidental
7. attorney in fact
8. operation of law
9. ostensible
10. estoppel
11. gratuitous
12. general
13. special
14. del credere
15. Ratification
16. signing the memorandum

True-False
1. False
2. True
3. False
4. False
5. True
6. True
7. True
8. True
9. True
10. False
11. False
12. True

Answers to Problems

1. Hipp is an agent. He is to act for his principal by exercising discretion in bringing about a contractual relationship between his principal and the third person.

2. Yes. Brent was authorized to draw checks. Brent was not authorized, however, to misappropriate money. The bank had no way of knowing that the proceeds of the check would be misappropriated. Brent was exercising his apparent authority. As between the department store and the bank, the department store is estopped to deny the authority of Brent.

3. No. Myers, the infant-principal, may disaffirm, or rescind, the sale although the agent was an adult. The agent is generally not a party to the contract. The principal is a party to the contract, and, like most infants, he can disaffirm the contract of sale and recover his money.

4. No. The attempted ratification by Williams was itself ineffective. A principal cannot ratify the unauthorized act of another person unless that person purports to act as agent for, and in the name of, the principal.

5. No. The note is void. Acts which are absolutely void cannot be ratified.

Chapter 34. Principal and Third Person

Fill-in Questions	True-False
1. implied	1. False
2. money	2. True
3. ready, willing, and able	3. False
4. undisclosed	4. False
5. disclosed	5. True
6. ministerial; mechanical	6. True
7. dual enterprise	7. False
8. course and scope of his authority	8. False

Answers to Problems

1. Yes. It is generally held that authority to appoint a subagent may exist where the nature of the business is such that it must be contemplated by the principal that the authority conferred on the agent will be exercised through subagents.

2. No. In this instance, it was the custom for customers to pay at the check-out place. This place should have been obvious to everyone, including Stone.

3. No. B.B. Brown did not disclose that he was acting as an agent. It is the duty of the agent to disclose his principal if he would avoid personal liability.

4. No. The agent-manager committed the tort of libel in an effort to further the business of the principal, and it was not an extreme deviation from the normal conduct of such an agent.

5. Yes. This agent was not authorized to collect money or other property in payment of the merchandise ordered. The defendant knew, or should have known, that payment to the agent with suits is not the proper type of contract which the agent is authorized to create. A traveling salesman with authority to solicit orders and send them to the home office has no authority to accept the offer or to receive payment in any form.

Chapter 35. Agent and Third Person

Fill-in Questions	True-False
1. incompetent; nonexistent	1. False
2. personally	2. False
3. personal liability	3. False
4. deceit	4. False
5. jointly; severally	5. True
6. implied warranty	6. True

7. fiduciary
8. tort
9. undisclosed
10. tortious
11. descriptio personae
12. del credere

Answers to Problems

1. Yes. The agent has a beneficial interest in the contract. It may be pointed out, however, that if the agent sues the third person and gets a judgment which is satisfied, the agent will hold the proceeds in a fiduciary or trust capacity for the principal. This agent is probably a del credere agent.

2. No. The agent did not assume liability. The Farmers Market knew that the agent was an agent for the farmer, because a part of the purchase price was paid directly to the farmer. The agent did not make any promises with respect to the vegetables.

3. Yes. The agent is liable where he fraudulently or otherwise wrongfully induces a third person to pay money over to him for his principal. The agent is liable to the third person even though the money was paid over to the principal.

4. Yes. The agent assumed the liability. The agent will be held liable when it clearly appears that it was the intention of the agent to assume the obligation as a personal liability and that he knew that credit was extended to him alone.

Chapter 36. Principal and Agent

Fill-in Questions
1. indemnity
2. interest; security
3. constructive
4. actual
5. dual capacity
6. sudden emergency
7. account
8. secret
9. privileged
10. exclusive; exclusive
11. will

True-False
1. True
2. False
3. True
4. False
5. True
6. False
7. True
8. False

Answers to Problems

1. No. Acts of a former agent with apparent continuing authority will, revocation notwithstanding, continue to bind the former principal to third persons unless proper notice is given.

2. The amount that the services are reasonably worth. In the absence of an agreement to pay for the services of the agent, the law implies a promise on the part of the principal to pay what the services are reasonably worth.

3. Assuming this is not an agency coupled with an interest and that the agent is not actively negotiating for a sale on a commission, the principal has the power to terminate the agency. The agent, however, could bring an action for breach of contract. The principal, although he has the power to do so, could not wrongfully discharge the agent without subjecting himself to liability for damages to the agent.

4. Yes. Insanity of the principal normally terminates the agency. The tenants were charged with notice of the insanity because the principal had been judicially declared insane.

5. Yes. The agent may not go into business for himself or work for a competitor and carry with him secret information, such as a list of customers or other trade secrets.

Chapter 37. Partnership: Nature, Creation, Property

Fill-in Questions	True-False
1. dormant	1. False
2. joint adventure	2. True
3. ostensible	3. False
4. trading; nontrading	4. False
5. general; limited	5. True
6. at will	6. True
7. personal	7. False
8. goodwill	8. True
9. partnership property	9. False
10. fictitious	10. False

Answers to Problems

1. Yes. The agreement contains all the essential elements of a partnership as contained in the Uniform Partnership Act. It is (1) an association (2) of two or more persons (3) to carry on a business (4) as co-owners (5) for profit.

2. No. This was the individual property of Aaron. Loans and accumulated undivided profits are individual property of a partner.

3. No. This was a nonprofit association. In order to create a partnership, the purpose of the business must be for a profit. The associates must share in the profits.

4. The answer depends on the intention of the partners. The agreement, however, seems to indicate that it was intended that the land be partnership property. Whether or not property given to the partnership for use is dedicated to the partnership or is to remain individual property is governed by the agreement of the partners.

5. A court of equity will regard and protect realty as partnership property and will direct the holder of the legal title to make such disposition of the realty as may be necessary to protect the equitable rights of Smith. Unless a contrary intention appears, property acquired with partnership funds is partnership property.

Chapter 38. Partnership: Relation to Third Persons

Fill-in Questions	True-False
1. scope of the partnership business	1. False
2. directly; specifically	2. True
3. Customary	3. True
4. Admissions; representations	4. False
5. mutual agency	5. True
	6. True
	7. True

Answers to Problems

1. Clark. Clark had an insurable interest in the inventory. A partner as co-owner of the business has an insurable interest in the partnership property. He may, therefore, take fire and other insurance on the specific partnership property, the proceeds of which are payable to him personally in case of loss.

2. Yes. A nonacting partner is liable for acts committed by an acting partner when the partnership is engaged in a criminal business.

3. No. A partner does not have the implied authority to sell partnership property used in the partnership business.

4. An unauthorized conveyance by Burke to an innocent purchaser for value would pass good title. Hill would have the right to have an unauthorized conveyance

set aside if the purchaser knew or should have known that the title was held for the partnership. A conveyance by the first purchaser to a second purchaser for value without knowledge, however, passes good title.

5. The acts enumerated are assigning the partnership property for the benefit of creditors; disposing of the goodwill of the business; performing any other act that would make it impossible to carry on the ordinary business of the partnership; confessing a judgment; and submitting a partnership claim to arbitration.

Chapter 39. Partners: Relation to One Another

Fill-in Questions	True-False
1. contribution	1. False
2. advances; capital	2. True
3. equitable conversion	3. True
4. indemnify	4. False
5. specific; tenant	5. True
6. interest	6. True
7. charging order	7. False
8. secret	8. True

Answers to Problems

1. Yes. Clark does not have access to the partnership books. A partner is entitled to a formal accounting whenever the circumstances render it just and reasonable.

2. No. The Partnership Act specifically provides that an assignment does not of itself entitle the assignee to interfere in the management of the partnership business.

3. The Uniform Partnership Act declares that on the death of a partner his right in specific partnership property vests in the surviving partner or partners for partnership purposes and that the partner's right in specific partnership property is not subject to dower, curtesy, or allowances to widows, heirs, or next of kin.

4. No. Morris should make a full disclosure. Each partner is required to make a full disclosure of all material facts within his knowledge relating to partnership affairs.

5. No. All partners, in the absence of an agreement to the contrary, have equal rights in the conduct and management of the partnership.

Chapter 40. Partnership: Dissolution, Winding Up, Termination

Fill-in Questions	True-False
1. marshaling assets	1. True
2. winding up	2. True
3. dissolution	3. False
4. at will	4. True
5. immediate dissolution	5. False
6. Termination	6. False
7. receiver	7. True
	8. False
	9. True

Answers to Problems

1. No. The Partnership Act provides that the partners who have not caused the dissolution of the partnership wrongfully may continue the business in the same name until the agreed term has expired provided they pay the withdrawing partner the value of his interest in the partnership.

2. Neither. The two sets of creditors share in the assets of the partnership on an equal basis.

3. The Uniform Partnership Act imposes a liability upon each partner for any contract entered into by one of the partners after dissolution if the acting partner had no knowledge of the dissolution where it is caused by an act of any partner. Brown would have no liability on the contract entered into by Smith, because Smith knew of Brown's withdrawal. Brown would be liable for his share of the contract entered into by Jones, because Jones did not know of the withdrawal.

4. Aaron. The right to wind up the partnership business is vested in the nonbankrupt partners where the dissolution is caused by the bankruptcy of one of the partners.

5. Linder, Lyle, and Lawson should each pay $5,000. The partners should bear the loss equally. Each will stand a total loss of $10,000.

6. A purchaser of a partner's interest in the partnership may apply for dissolution of the partnership when the interest was assigned if the partnership is a partnership at will.

Chapter 41. Limited Partnership

Fill-in Questions
1. surname
2. creditors; limited; general
3. services
4. partnership business

True-False
1. False
2. True
3. False
4. False

Chapter 42. Corporations: Introduction; Promoters

Fill-in Questions
1. corporate entity
2. close
3. charter
4. de jure; de facto
5. domestic; foreign
6. incorporators
7. secret
8. adoption

True-False
1. False
2. True
3. True
4. True
5. False
6. False
7. True
8. True
9. False
10. False
11. False
12. True

Answers to Problems
1. Brown will not succeed. He must look to the corporation for repayment. A corporation is a legal entity separate and distinct from its shareholders.

2. Decision for the corporation. The organization of a corporation properly organized in pursuance of a not-for-profit statute is a convenient method of holding property.

3. No. The Tennis Club was a nonprofit unincorporated association. A nonprofit unincorporated association is formed to advance the members, and being unincorporated, lacks the capacity to hold title to real property.

4. No. A corporation is not a citizen within the meaning of Article 4, Section 2, of the United States Constitution with respect to the privileges of citizens in the several states.

5. To the state of its incorporation, a corporation is a domestic corporation; to all other states and countries, it is a foreign corporation. For example, to the State of Delaware, a corporation incorporated in Delaware is a domestic corporation, but other states would refer to such corporation as a foreign corporation.

6. At the first formal meeting, officers and directors are generally elected, the form of the share certificate and the corporate seal are adopted, subscriptions to shares of stock are accepted, and such other acts are performed as are necessary to the actual beginning of business.

7. To plan the organization of the corporation, to solicit its shares of stock, to acquire property for its use, to negotiate contracts for its operation, to complete the actual incorporation process, and to perform all other activities necessary to establish the corporation for the prosecution of its business.

Chapter 43. Corporations: Corporate Financial Structure

Fill-in Questions
1. creditor; debt
2. par-value shares
3. cumulative
4. participating
5. owner; equity
6. No-par-value
7. noncumulative
8. watered stock
9. warrant
10. split-up
11. compulsory-redemption

True-False
1. True
2. False
3. True
4. True
5. False
6. False
7. True

Answers to Problems

1. Wilcox is bound. An agreement among a number of persons to form a corporation and to subscribe to its authorized capital stock is generally held to constitute a contract between the subscribers themselves.

2. No. Bankruptcy of the corporation will excuse the purchaser for the unpaid balance in this problem even against the claim of creditors.

3. The purchaser will not be excused. Bankruptcy of the corporation will not excuse the purchaser against creditors.

4. The answer depends upon whether the preferred shares are cumulative or noncumulative. Dividends are held to be impliedly cumulative unless a contrary intention appears.

5. Equally. The preferred shareholders will participate proportionately with the common shareholders in the remaining surplus.

6. True value rule: The holder of watered shares is liable to creditors, and the element of fraud or good faith is not essential. Good faith rule: The shareholder or promoter is protected as against creditors if both parties believed that the consideration given is equal to the par value of the stock taken in exchange for it.

Chapter 44. Corporations: Powers

Fill-in Questions
1. inherent
2. treasury
3. piercing the corporate veil
4. ultra vires

True-False
1. True
2. False
3. True
4. True

5. express	5. True
6. intra vires	6. False
	7. False
	8. False

Answers to Problems

1. Yes. It would be in the furtherance of the business of the corporation to sell electricity. The Electric Company would therefore have the implied power to sell electrical appliances.

2. No. It is no defense that the act constituting the offense was ultra vires.

3. No. This was an executory ultra vires contract, and the majority of the courts will not permit any party to maintain an action on such a contract.

4. Shareholders are permitted to bring an injunction proceedings against the corporation; the state may bring proceedings against the corporation; the corporation may bring actions against its officers and directors; and the doctrine of ultra vires has sometimes been abolished as a defense.

5. No. A corporation may form a subsidiary in order to accomplish a legitimate business purpose.

Chapter 45. Corporations: Relation to Directors and Officers

Fill-in Questions	**True-False**
1. outsider; insiders	1. False
2. Interlocking directorates	2. True
3. share dividends	3. False
4. dividend certificate	4. True
5. interested director	5. False
6. scrip	6. False
	7. True
	8. True
	9. True
	10. True
	11. False
	12. True

Answers to Problems

1. No. Dividends cannot lawfully be declared until the corporation pays or provides for the payment of its debts.

2. Yes. The negligence of the directors in signing the checks does not comply with the standard of care required of a director.

3. The amount of the dividend, the date when it will be paid, the medium of payment, the classes of shareholders to whom it is payable, and the record date to determine the time when the shareholders of record shall be ascertained.

4. Electing and removing directors, accepting and amending the corporate charter, adopting and amending the bylaws, merging or consolidating the corporation with another corporation, altering the authorized stock structure, transferring all of of the property of the corporation, and voluntarily dissolving the corporation.

5. A distribution to the shareholder in the form of notes or promises to pay the amount of the dividend at a certain future time is known as a scrip dividend. It is generally declared when the corporation has a surplus but not sufficient cash to pay a cash dividend.

6. Dividends which are paid to shareholders while the corporation is insolvent, or rendered insolvent, are recoverable from the shareholders.

Chapter 46. Corporations: Relation to Shareholders

Fill-in Questions
1. proxy
2. voting trust certificate
3. cumulative
4. bona fide purchaser
5. pre-emptive right
6. issuer
7. registrar

True-False
1. True
2. True
3. False
4. False
5. False
6. True
7. True
8. True
9. False

Answers to Problems

1. The right to share in the profits of the corporation by way of dividends, the right to share in the assets upon dissolution, the right to vote, and the remedial rights.

2. Decision for the creditor. A creditor who has an unsatisfied judgment against the corporation may proceed against the shareholders for the unpaid balance of their subscriptions.

3. No. Notice of the time and place of holding regular meetings, as a general rule, is not required when the time and place is fixed by the bylaws.

4. No. The pre-emptive right, as a general rule, does not exist in shares issued for services or for property instead of cash, nor in shares to effect a consolidation or merger.

5. The shareholder may sue the corporation in his individual capacity. This is neither a representative nor a derivative suit. The latter two types of suits are class suits. The shareholder who sues the corporation for $10,000 is suing on his own behalf only.

6. That his transfer is effective and rightful; that the security is genuine and has not been materially altered; and that he knows of no fact which might impair the validity of the security.

7. It is the duty of the transfer agent to record the transfer, cancel the surrendered certificate, and issue a new certificate in the name of the transferee.

Chapter 47. Corporations: Termination

Fill-in Questions
1. dissolved
2. consolidation
3. merger
4. voluntary; involuntary

True-False
1. True
2. False
3. True
4. True

PART 9: SECURITIES REGULATION; ANTITRUST; LABOR RELATIONS

Chapter 48. Securities Regulation

Fill-in Questions
1. $500,000
2. prospectus; prospectus
3. arbitrage
4. cash tender
5. blue sky

True-False
1. True
2. False
3. True
4. False
5. True

6. equity security	6. False
7. restricted security	7. False
8. affiliate	8. False
9. takeover	9. True
10. Securities; Exchange	10. False

Answers to Problems

1. No. The corporation would be exempted from the provisions of regulation C. The corporation, however, would be subject to the simplified procedure for small offerings. This procedure is governed by regulation A.

2. No. Brown would be required to file an application for registration and listing with the exchange. The Exchange Act requires registration, but the exchanges generally require that a separate listing application be filed.

3. Davis would be required to report this purchase to the Securities and Exchange Commission. It is provided that any person, within ten days after acquiring directly or indirectly the beneficial ownership of more than 5 percent of a class of any registered equity security, shall file with the Commission the information contained in schedule 13D and shall also send a copy thereof to the issuer and to any exchange on which the securities are listed.

4. The corporation should use an offering circular. The corporation was incorporated within one year prior to the date of filing the notification and had not had a net income. Such securities involve a greater risk to the investor than do issues of well-established issuers.

5. The disclosure type of statute provides that any circular, prospectus, or other advertising material must disclose all the essential facts with respect to the security offered. The antifraud type of statute prohibits fraud in the sale of securities, provides remedies to defrauded persons, and imposes criminal penalties. The broker-dealer type of statute, as a condition to engage in the business of buying and selling securities, requires brokers and dealers to procure a license.

Chapter 49. Antitrust: Monopolies, Restraints of Trade, Conspiracies

Fill-in Questions	True-False
1. price maintenance	1. False
2. horizontal	2. True
3. conglomerate	3. True
4. Chain Store	4. False
5. nonsigner	5. False
6. Sherman	6. True
7. assets	7. True
8. fair trade	8. False
9. vertical	9. True
10. conglomerate	10. False

Answers to Problems

1. The Hardware Company could bring a civil action for treble damages against the corporation, plus court costs and reasonable attorney's fees.

2. Decision for the customers. The Robinson-Patman Act makes it illegal to pay for or furnish a customer with displays of goods and demonstrations unless such displays and demonstrations are made available on a proportionately equal basis to all purchasers—small as well as large purchasers. It is not necessary to show that competition has been lessened.

3. Yes. Brown knew that the price he received was lower than the price received by other customers. Section 2(f) of the Robinson-Patman Act makes it illegal

for a buyer to knowingly induce or receive a discrimination in price which is prohibited by section 2(a).

4. Yes. Acquisitions of assets, as well as stock, are prohibited by the Cellar-Kefauver Act.

5. Around the turn of the century, corporations engaged in the same type of business, through the use of a trust agreement, transferred the stock in each company to a board of trustees. The board of trustees under this trust arrangement could monopolize trade and conspire in restraint of trade.

Chapter 50. Labor Relations

Fill-in Questions
1. intellectual
2. collectively
3. featherbedding
4. yellow dog
5. National
6. primary
7. hot-cargo
8. right-to-work

True-False
1. False
2. True
3. True
4. False
5. True
6. False
7. False
8. False
9. True
10. False

Answers to Problems

1. The President of the United States could ask the court for an injunction ordering the union to suspend the strike for eighty days.

2. Yes. The Landrum-Griffin Act accords union members the right, upon request, to be given a copy of the collective bargaining agreement that they work under.

3. No. The Fair Labor Standards Act regulates hours and wages of employees in commerce or in the production of goods for commerce.

4. The stated purpose of the Occupational Safety and Health Act is to assure, as far as possible, every man and woman in the nation safe and healthful working conditions.

5. The term "employer" as defined by the Employment Security Amendments Act of 1970 means a person who meets either of two conditions: (1) he employs one or more employees on each of some twenty days during the calendar year, or (2) he pays wages of $1,500 or more during a calendar quarter.

PART 10: PROPERTY

Chapter 51. Introduction to Property

Fill-in Questions
1. tangible
2. estate by the entirety
3. joint tenancy
4. eminent domain
5. intangible

True-False
1. False
2. False
3. True
4. True
5. False

Chapter 52. The Nature of Personal Property

Fill-in Questions
1. inter vivos
2. adjunction
3. freehold

True-False
1. True
2. True
3. False

4. Chattels personal
5. causa mortis
6. specification
7. nonfreehold
8. Chattels personal
9. Accession

4. True
5. True
6. False
7. True

Answers to Problems

1. The finder. The finder could bring replevin for the purpose of acquiring possession of the ring. Since the place where the ring was found is not in dispute, the general rule that a finder of lost property is entitled to its possession as against everyone but the true owner would be applicable.

2. No. This was an executed gift inter vivos, and a gift inter vivos, once executed, is irrevocable.

3. No. The title to abandoned property may be acquired by the first person who reduces it to his control and possession with the intent to take dominion over the article.

4. Aaron, the wrongdoer, must show that the per unit value of the commingled mass is equal to, or greater than, the per unit value of that of the innocent party. Aaron also has the burden of proving the respective shares of each party and the value of the olive oil.

Chapter 53. The Nature of Real Property

Fill-in Questions
1. quit-claim deed
2. Accretion
3. riparian
4. Percolating water
5. avulsion
6. Surface
7. Lateral support
8. appurtenant
9. profit a prendre
10. in gross
11. Torrens System
12. fee simple; fee simple absolute
13. base; qualified
14. dower; curtesy
15. executory limitation
16. reversion
17. grantor; grantee

True-False
1. True
2. False
3. True
4. False
5. True
6. True
7. False
8. True
9. False
10. True
11. False
12. False
13. True
14. False
15. True

Answers to Problems

1. The icehouse is personal property of the tenant which he may remove upon termination of the lease. The understanding between the tenant and the owner of the land indicates that it was intended that the icehouse remain the personal property of the tenant.

2. The heirs of Brown. A fee-simple estate descends to the heirs of the owner upon the death of the owner if it has not been transferred by will.

3. (1) A fee simple subject to a condition subsequent. (2) No. The land belongs to Jones. The interest left in Jones, the grantor, is a right of entry for condition broken.

4. A reversion. A reversion is a future estate left in the grantor. The property will ultimately revert to the heirs of Brown.

5. (1) Executory limitation. (2) The land will vest in Mary upon the graduation of Aaron, Jr., from college. The executory limitation is subject to a condition precedent and does not vest until the condition is performed.

6. A remainder differs from an executory interest in that the estate preceding the remainder—frequently called the particular estate—may not be a fee simple.

7. An easement is appurtenant when it is created to benefit the possession of adjoining land, and an easement in gross is one which is not created to benefit the possessor of adjoining land.

8. Yes. An owner who pays the contractor who does not pay subcontractors, laborers, and materialmen may be required to pay such persons. These persons are entitled to a mechanic's lien against the premises.

Chapter 54. Landlord and Tenant

Fill-in Questions
1. tenancy for years
2. lessor
3. periodic tenancy
4. lessee
5. sufferance
6. tenancy at will
7. waste
8. surrender

True-False
1. False
2. True
3. False
4. False
5. True
6. True
7. True
8. False
9. True

Answers to Problems

1. No. This was an apartment. The destruction of the building in which an apartment is located by fire or other casualty terminates the lease.

2. No. A tenancy for years is a tenancy less than a freehold for a fixed period. A lease, the duration of which is not certain to happen, is not a lease for a fixed period.

3. Three remedies are available: The tenant may treat the lease as at an end, or he may take possession at a later date, or he may bring an action to obtain possession.

4. No. A tenancy at will is terminated by the death of the landlord or the tenant. A tenancy at sufferance terminates when the landlord ejects the tenant or recognizes him as a tenant.

5. Decision for the sublessees. A lessee, in the absence of a covenant or statute to the contrary, may generally assign his interest in the term, or he may sublease the premises. Between the sublessee and the original lessor there is no privity of contract. The sublessee, therefore, incurs no liability directly to the original lessor because of the subletting.

6. A lease may be terminated by death where its terms are so personal as to apply to the lessee only.

Chapter 55. Real Estate Mortgages

Fill-in Questions
1. trustor; lender; trustee
2. lien theory
3. mortgagee
4. mortgagor
5. obligatory; optional
6. judicial sale

True-False
1. False
2. True
3. False
4. True
5. True
6. False
7. True

Answers to Problems

1. Davis has a superior claim to the 80 acres according to the prevailing rule. The after-acquired property clause creates an equitable lien as soon as the mortgagor

acquires the property. Such a lien will be good against all third persons except bona fide purchasers without notice of the mortgage and prior lienors.

2. The chief duties of Jones, the trustee, are to sell the land upon default at public auction to the highest bidder and, after satisfying the mortgage debt and expenses of sale, to account to the trustor as to any remaining surplus.

3. The vendee in an installment land contract is usually given possession of the land, but he does not acquire title until he has paid the last installment.

4. The rule which represents the majority takes the view that, since the mortgagee is not bound by constructive notice of junior liens, he is protected as to all advances he makes while ignorant of such liens. The other rule takes the view that since the mortgagee is not bound to make a later advance, he is required to search the record for intervening liens. The courts distinguish between obligatory and optional advances. If the advance is obligatory, the mortgagee will have priority whether he has constructive notice or actual notice when he makes the advance.

PART 11: WILLS AND TRUSTS

Chapter 56. Wills and Estates of Decedents

Fill-in Questions
1. testamentary age
2. Ademption
3. Abatement
4. personal representative
5. probate; surrogate's
6. administrator; administratrix
7. testate, interstate
8. executor; executrix
9. letters testamentary
10. holographic will
11. nuncupative will
12. per stirpes; per capita

True-False
1. False
2. True
3. False
4. True
5. True
6. False
7. False

Answers to Problems
1. Yes. The states that do acknowledge a nuncupative will generally limit the privilege to personal property. Real property, therefore, cannot pass by nuncupation.

2. An executor may prove a will by a statement of the witnesses, under oath, that the instrument offered for probate is the same instrument to which they subscribed their names as witnesses.

3. The overall duties of the personal representative are to discover and collect the assets of the decedent, pay the lawful claims against the estate, and distribute the balance to the persons entitled thereto.

4. A surviving descendant is one who is in line of descent from the decedent. The expression includes children, grandchildren, and other descendants. Surviving ascendants include persons to whom one is related in an ascending line, such as parents and grandparents. Collaterals include those belonging to the same ancestral stock but not in a direct line of descent, such as brothers, cousins, uncles, and nephews.

5. No. Mary Brown, as a tenant by the entirety, may dispense with administration. The interest of her husband passed by survivorship to her.

6. The generally accepted formula for determining mental capacity is that a person need not possess superior or even average mentality, but that he must be capable of understanding and carrying on in his mind in a general way (a) the nature

and extent of his property, (b) the persons who are the natural objects of his bounty, (c) the disposition he is making of his property, (d) an appreciation of these elements in relation to each other, so that he may (e) form an orderly desire as to the disposition of his property.

Chapter 57. Trusts

Fill-in Questions

1. res
2. settlor
3. cy pres power
4. Rule against Perpetuities
5. testamentary
6. Totten; poor-man's
7. spendthrift
8. charitable
9. resulting; constructive
10. constructive
11. passive; simple, dry; naked
12. worthier title

True-False

1. True
2. False
3. True
4. True
5. True
6. True
7. False
8. False
9. True
10. True
11. False

Answers to Problems

1. The refusal of Cabot to serve as trustee does not alter the rights of the son with respect to the land. Equity will not allow a trust to fail for want of a trustee. The court will appoint a trustee if the named trustee declines the position.

2. No. Cabot could not, in the absence of a power of revocation in the trust agreement, change the beneficiary.

3. Yes. The settlor cannot name himself as a beneficiary of a spendthrift trust on the theory that to do so would offer too large a possibility for defrauding creditors.

4. No. A trustee who has once accepted the trust cannot resign at will. The usual method of resignation is by application to the court.

5. No. In order to create a trust, the res must be definite and ascertainable. Davis, the so-called trustor, had not dedicated a proper res.

6. (1) The College Club cannot qualify as a trustee because a nonincorporated association cannot hold title to property. (2) No. The court will appoint a trustee. A trust will not fail for the lack of a trustee.

7. Trusts for the establishment of pension funds, and profit sharing trusts by corporations for the benefit of their employees. The rule is also not ordinarily applied to charitable trusts.

PART 12: INSURANCE; SURETYSHIP; GUARANTY; BANKRUPTCY

Chapter 58. The Insurance Contract

Fill-in Questions

1. whole life; regular life
2. floater
3. affirmative
4. promissory
5. at and from
6. special agent
7. interim receipt; memorandum of agreement; binding slip

True-False

1. True
2. False
3. True
4. False
5. True
6. True
7. False

8. barratry
9. insurer; insured
10. jettison

8. False
9. True
10. True
11. False
12. True

Answers to Problems

1. Yes, but the decisions are not entirely uniform. As a general rule, however, any person may become a party to a contract of insurance provided the person is competent to enter into a contract and possesses an insurable interest in the subject of the insurance.

2. Yes. It seems unquestioned today that a husband has an insurable interest in the life of his wife.

3. Decision for the insurance company. Davis was under a duty to disclose the existence of the fire. Concealment in bad faith with intent to defraud renders the contract voidable.

4. The courts will not permit the insured to show by parol evidence that the agent of the insurer was told one thing and that the agent placed a different or false answer in the application if the entire-contract provision is applicable or if the application contains an agreement that the applicant has read the statements and that they are correct. Many courts will, however, permit the insured to introduce evidence to support an estoppel against the insurer. The facts in this problem, however, do not indicate an estoppel.

5. The policy and the application constitute the entire contract between the parties. Many policies contain an entire-contract provision, and some states have enacted entire-contract statutes. The courts generally hold that the insured is under a duty to read his policy and the copy of the attached application.

6. The chief distinction between representations and warranties is that representations are inducements to enter into the contract; warranties are a part of the contract. The insurer must prove representations to be material; warranties are conclusively presumed to be material.

Chapter 59. Standard Policies and Provisions

Fill-in Questions
1. pro rata
2. incontestible
3. vacancy
4. mortgage
5. valued-policy
6. coinsurance
7. rider

True-False
1. False
2. False
3. True
4. True
5. True
6. True
7. True
8. False
9. True
10. False

Answers to Problems

1. The purpose of the diminished liability clause is to avoid forfeiture of the policy and permit the insured to recover indemnity proportionate to the hazard of the new employment.

2. The total amount of damage. The courts hold that the insurer is liable for the total amount of the damage if the explosion was caused by a preceding fire.

3. Under the terms of the iron-safe clause, the insured agrees to take a complete itemized inventory at least once a year, or within one month after the policy is issued

if the inventory has not been taken within the past year; to keep a set of books showing all sales; to keep such books securely locked in a fireproof safe at night and at all other times when the building mentioned in the policy is not open for business; and to produce the books for inspection of the insurer if a loss occurs.

4. $10,000 from each company if the policy had a pro rata clause. He cannot recover anything if the policy had an overinsurance clause.

5. The standard policy requires the insured to give immediate written notice to the insurer; to protect the property from further damage; to separate the damaged from the undamaged personal property; to furnish an inventory of destroyed, damaged, and undamaged property; and to furnish the insurer, within sixty days, a proof of loss.

Chapter 60. Nature of Suretyship and Guaranty

Fill-in Questions
1. official
2. debtor; creditor; surety
3. indemnitor
4. common-law; statutory
5. performance
6. payment
7. Fidelity
8. guarantor

True-False
1. True
2. True
3. False
4. False
5. True
6. False

Answers to Problems

1. Injunction bonds, attachment bonds, replevin bonds, bail bonds, and appeal bonds.

2. The liability of an indorser is conditional and secondary because he agrees to pay only where demand is made on the maker and notice of dishonor is given to him; the undertaking of the surety is primary.

3. No. This was a general guaranty. Any creditor who has knowledge of the guaranty and extends credit in reliance thereon may enforce the guaranty.

4. (1) An absolute guaranty. (2) Aaron, Sr., must pay the $1,000. The liability of an absolute guarantor becomes fixed upon default of the debtor; no other event or condition, including notice to the guarantor, is required.

5. An indemnitor contracts to save another party harmless from some legal consequence; a surety undertakes to pay or perform if the principal debtor does not.

Chapter 61. Rights and Defenses of the Surety

Fill-in Questions
1. exoneration
2. subrogation
3. reimbursement
4. limitations
5. contribution
6. creditor

True-False
1. False
2. True
3. True
4. True
5. True
6. True
7. False
8. True
9. True

Answers to Problems

1. Yes. The courts agree that the surety is discharged. The recent cases hold, however, that he is discharged only to the extent of the value of the consideration at the time it is returned.

298

2. No. As soon as the debt is due, Brown could bring a suit in equity and compel his cosureties to pay their pro rata share.

3. Bart is discharged. The surety, according to the general rule, will be discharged by any material change in the contract existing between the debtor and the creditor. Any alteration in the amount would be material.

4. Yes. An extension of time of payment given by the creditor to the debtor will discharge the surety. The surety is not discharged, however, if he consents to the extension; nor is he discharged if the creditor expressly reserves his rights against the surety.

5. Yes. The right of reimbursement is essentially the same with respect to a surety and a guarantor. A surety who has made payment is entitled to demand reimbursement from the principal for the amount which he has paid. This is eminently fair.

Chapter 62. Bankruptcy

Fill-in Questions
1. adjudication
2. Straight; ordinary
3. referee
4. receiver
5. trustee
6. reclamation
7. wage earner
8. corporate reorganization; arrangements; wage earner's plans
9. district
10. six
11. four
12. three
13. corporations
14. four
15. three

True-False
1. True
2. True
3. True
4. False
5. False
6. True
7. False
8. True
9. False
10. False
11. True
12. True
13. False
14. True
15. False

Answers to Problems

1. The balance sheet test of insolvency means that there is an excess of liabilities over assets at a fair valuation. The equity test means the inability of the debtor to pay his debts as they mature.

2. Municipal, railroad, insurance, banking corporations, building and loan associations, farmers, and wage earners.

3. No. This is a way in which Brown can avoid having to go into involuntary bankruptcy. If he does commit an act of bankruptcy, one of his creditors could file an involuntary petition. This would have to be done within four months after the commission of an act of bankruptcy.

4. (a) Yes. This is a fixed liability which is evidenced by an instrument in writing. The debt is absolutely owing, but it does not have to be due at the time the petition is filed. (b) This claim is provable. A provable claim is one that may be asserted and allowed against a bankrupt estate. This claim is entitled to share pro rata in the distribution of dividends, and a claim that is provable is discharged as a general rule. If Smith fails to file his claim, it will be discharged.

5. No. The father reasonably thought that Byers was solvent. If the father had known of the insolvency of Byers, the trustee could set the conveyance aside since it occurred within four months immediately prior to the filing of the petition.